ATOMIC ENERGY
IN THE
SOVIET UNION

ATOMIC ENERGY
IN THE
SOVIET UNION

ARNOLD KRAMISH
THE RAND CORPORATION

STANFORD UNIVERSITY PRESS
STANFORD, CALIFORNIA
LONDON: OXFORD UNIVERSITY PRESS
1959

STANFORD UNIVERSITY PRESS
STANFORD, CALIFORNIA
LONDON: OXFORD UNIVERSITY PRESS
© 1959 BY THE RAND CORPORATION
LIBRARY OF CONGRESS CATALOG CARD NUMBER: 59-14724
PRINTED IN THE UNITED STATES OF AMERICA

TO SARAH AND JOHN
MY PARENTS

FOREWORD

Following World War II, the United States and Great
Britain issued comprehensive reports on the historical and
technical development of their atomic energy programs.
These have since been supplemented by periodic progress
reports. No similar information has been made available by
the government of the USSR. It is the purpose of this book
to correct the deficiency.

In doing so the author has attempted to present a technical and political analysis as unbiased as the data permit.
It is hoped that the resulting text, when describing a particular decision or achievement, will not be taken out of
context to indicate Soviet superiority or inferiority. Also,
as is emphasized several times in the text, there are strong
recognized differences in economic and political outlook between the USSR and the West, and a simple comparison of
technical achievement more often than not fails in itself to
give the true story. Wherever possible in this study the

political and economic motives have been correlated with the technical data. Admittedly, some of the inferences may be somewhat in error and, if responsible Soviet authorities wish to break their silence, corrections would be most welcome. The scientific analyses are as precise as the Soviet statements on which they are based.

Assembled from the meager scraps of information found during the systematic scanning of many thousands of issues of Soviet newspapers and technical journals, the account given here is believed to present close to the maximum amount of information publicly available and of interest to the general reader. The specialized reader is already aware of the more detailed technical data that can be found in various Soviet scientific journals, but again, these articles represent a narrow selection from the entire body of Soviet nuclear research and development.

This book represents an extensively revised and current version of three research memoranda previously published by The RAND Corporation as a part of its research program for the United States Air Force. The first of these memoranda was co-authored with Melville J. Ruggles, now vice-president of the Council on Library Resources, Inc. For the early collaborative effort and the stimulating conversations on Soviet decision-making processes, the author is most grateful to Mr. Ruggles. Anne M. Jonas provided knowledgeable research assistance, and it is a pleasure to acknowledge her important contribution. To the many others, within RAND and without, whose discussions and comments on draft sections were of considerable benefit to the author, a final note of appreciation is due.

CONTENTS

ATOMIC ENERGY
IN THE
SOVIET UNION

1

THE ATOM AWAKENED

In 1760, Mikhail Lomonosov[1] wrote: "Physicists, and especially chemists, will have to operate in darkness unless they learn the inner imperceptible structure of particles." By the early 1890's, most well-informed people had come to believe that man had completely emerged from the darkness, that his understanding of the universe was approaching perfection. The ultimate component of matter, so it seemed, was the impenetrable, quiescent atom.

This complacency was short-lived. In the space of a few years, beginning in 1895, the discovery of X-rays and the detection of the radioactivity of uranium, radium, and other elements served to split the comfortably closed world of physics. None of the existing theories about matter or energy explained these new phenomena. Excitement was intense— not only among scientists, but also among the general public. Thus the mysterious energy in the nucleus of the atom startled the world fully fifty years before Hiroshima.

It was not long before speculation arose about the tremendous power, for good or evil, that could be obtained from the atomic nucleus. Science-fiction writers, of course, were the boldest prognosticators. H. G. Wells predicted in 1914 that radioactivity would be controlled and put to work for man by the 1950's. But this might not be an unmixed blessing:

Certainly it seems now that nothing could have been more obvious to the people of the early twentieth century than the rapidity with which war was becoming impossible. And as certainly they did not see it. They did not see it until the atomic bombs burst in their fumbling hands.[2]

The excitement and speculation about radioactivity were world-wide. They were evident in Russia, where in 1918 a science-fiction novel, *Red Star* by Aleksandr Bogdanov, spoke of the inhabitants of the planet Mars as enjoying an advanced stage of scientific and social development. Some Martians, in Bogdanov's novel, visited Earth in a spaceship powered by a force vaguely attributed to radioactive substances.

It remains to be seen whether Bogdanov's imagination was more or less clairvoyant than Wells'. The propulsive force in Bogdanov's Martian spaceship was derived from a "negative gravity" phenomenon caused, in a manner not explained, by radioactivity. Wells, in an almost uncanny guess, foresaw the role of a neutral particle, the neutron, in unlocking the power in the atom. He placed the discovery of this basic principle in the year 1933. It actually occurred in 1932.

Lecturing at Moscow about 1920, Bogdanov also developed the thesis that the most necessary prerequisite of socialism would be a highly concentrated source of energy available to small groups and individuals, and he concluded that the brightest prospect for achieving such energy lay in the atomic nucleus.

Bogdanov's visions about atomic energy must have been inspired by the findings of Western European scientists or science-fiction writers, for, so far as a rather cursory search shows, there was no significant nuclear research in progress in Russia before the early 1920's. Although there were able physicists in Russia before World War I, it seems that none of them was examining the problem of internal atomic phenomena with the same interest that was evident in the West, particularly at the Cavendish Laboratory at Cambridge, at Niels Bohr's Institute at Copenhagen, and at Göttingen. And the devastating war and revolution that followed no doubt delayed the beginning of Russian research in the field until the early 1920's.

Once started, however, Russian scientists seem to have been energetic in making up for lost time. In 1921, Peter L. Kapitsa, who had been lecturing at the Leningrad Polytechnic Institute, came to the Cavendish Laboratory at Cambridge University and worked directly with Lord Rutherford and with a number of the younger physicists who later were to be acclaimed as "pioneers" in nuclear science. He was thus at the center of the most active and creative work in this field, and it is, of course, almost certain that he informed his fellow scientists in the Soviet Union about the extremely interesting work being done by his Cambridge colleagues. It is known that he kept in close touch with his scientific friends in the Soviet Union, and he probably would have been sympathetic and cooperative toward their efforts to develop nuclear research in Russia. It should be noted, however, that Kapitsa himself worked for only a short time in the field of nuclear physics. His work with Rutherford on alpha particles lasted only a year. From 1922 onward his own research was concerned with magnetism and low temperatures.

Probably even more instrumental than Kapitsa in bringing the atomic findings of Western scientists into the Soviet

Union was V. I. Vernadskii, one of Russia's most distinguished scientists. He founded the State Radium Institute
at Leningrad in 1922 and was its director until 1939. In
1923, shortly after his appointment, he left the Soviet Union
for extended visits in Western Europe, including a lengthy
stay at Paris, where he engaged in experimental work in
Madame Curie's Radium Institute.

Vernadskii was not blind to the potentialities of the work
on which his new institute was embarking. In 1922 he wrote:

We are approaching a tremendous revolution in human life
with which nothing hitherto experienced can be compared.
It will not be long before man will receive atomic energy
for his disposal, a source of energy which will make it possible for him to build his life as he pleases.[3]

Nor, perhaps, was he blind to its military potentialities:
"Scientists ought not close their eyes to the possible consequence of their scientific work and of the scientific process.
They should feel responsible for the consequences of their
discoveries."[4]

Vernadskii's stature in Russian science was such that his
views would almost certainly have stimulated other scientists to begin or intensify work in nuclear physics.

The published record shows that Soviet nuclear research
in the decade after 1920 grew to significant proportions. The
most outstanding Soviet nuclear physicist of this period was
Dimitrii V. Skobel'tsyn, who in 1923 started research on the
measurement and detection of radioactivity. Soon thereafter
he began work on the production of secondary electrons resulting from the emission of radiation from the atom. In
the course of this work he was the first man to observe the
flight path of cosmic rays. This accidental observation was
made in a cloud chamber, a device that had been invented
a number of years earlier by C. T. R. Wilson, an English
physicist, to observe the rays from natural radioactive substances. The fundamental observations that Skobel'tsyn was

able to make as a result of this development were important to the early understanding of the nature of cosmic rays. Skobel'tsyn was also the first to observe a laboratory nuclear reaction caused in bombardment by cosmic particles.

Meanwhile, a group of scientists under Vitalii Grigorievich Khlopin at the Radium Institute was developing important techniques in the chemistry of radioactive substances in the course of its work on the extraction of radium from uranium ores. At about the same time, other scientists were making fundamental contributions to the theory of quantum mechanics. While they did not, at the time, apply their researches to the nucleus of the atom, the theoretical school that they founded provided a firm basis for the later, more intense excursions into the nuclear field.

Despite this considerable activity during the twenties, Soviet work in nuclear physics appears to have been somewhat haphazard and on a small scale, at least until 1930.

The year 1930, however, was a turning point for Soviet nuclear physics. In that year, the grand old man of Russian physics, Abram F. Ioffe, took an active interest in nuclear research. In his own words:

This happened in May 1930 at a time when our country was still comparatively poor and all efforts and means were directed at the fulfillment of the first Five-Year Plan. My colleagues at the [Physico-Technical] Institute and myself thought that it was essential to begin work on the atom nucleus. We were worried, however, because it was the middle of the year, when appropriations for our work had already been made, and the new researches we outlined required an additional expenditure of several hundred thousand rubles. I went to Sergei Ordzhonikidze, who was chairman of the Supreme Council of National Economy, put the matter before him, and in literally ten minutes left his office with an order signed by him to assign the sum I had requested to the Institute. Once started, we have continued work on the atomic nucleus for fifteen years as an essential part of our plan,[5]

This statement was made in June 1945, two months before Hiroshima. If it was a rewriting of history intended to
bolster the prestige of Soviet nuclear physicists in the face of
spectacular successes of scientists in the Manhattan Project,
it could have been inspired only by espionage data and not
by concern over the sensation caused by the dropping of
atom bombs on Japan. In any event, the history of Soviet
nuclear research in the 1930's demonstrates that it was not
necessary for Ioffe to exaggerate Soviet accomplishments in
the field.

It is regrettable that there is no other record of Ioffe's
ten-minute conversation with Ordzhonikidze. Our understanding of the next decade of Soviet nuclear research would
be much clearer if we knew what arguments Ioffe used to
obtain the funds needed for research.

A wry anecdote circulating among Soviet scientists described an alleged argument used by Ioffe to get these funds.
According to this story, the Soviet government was opposed
to financial support for nuclear physics on the ground that
this field was too far removed from the problems facing the
government. Ioffe, it was said, got around this objection
partly by pointing out that, from Democritus and Lucretius
to Marx and Engels, atomic theory was basic to a material-
istic interpretation of history, and by recalling that Marx's
own doctoral dissertation was on Democritus, the father of
atomic theory.

This story might well have contained a kernel of truth,
for the new Bolshevik regime was eager to find support for
the doctrine on which it was based. Many Soviet leaders,
Bukharin foremost among them, took an active, though sometimes misplaced, interest in scientific inquiry primarily because they hoped or expected that the findings would place
a firm foundation under the theory of dialectical materialism.

It is possible that Ioffe also promised the government that

atomic energy would be useful in the chemical and electrical industries, for he wrote of such a possibility at about the time he made his appeal. That particular promise, if it was made, took more than twenty years to fulfill. Two years after Ioffe's prediction, Lord Rutherford was still very pessimistic: "These transformations of the atom are of extraordinary interest to scientists but we cannot control atomic energy to an extent which would be of any value commercially, and I believe we are not likely ever to do so."[6]

The Soviet government's attitude toward atomic energy during 1930–41 could be more clearly understood if we knew more than we do about the Kremlin's attitude toward, and control over, science in general and nuclear physics in particular. Unfortunately, this subject has been neglected by Western students of Soviet affairs, and the relation between science and government in the USSR is not well understood in the West. We know that the Soviet government has frequently insisted that scientists keep their body of theoretical thought in conformity with the current official interpretation of Marxist dogma. We know that individual scientists have been punished for ideological nonconformity, or for perhaps even more serious sins, such as maintaining contact with Western scientists. But we do not have a clear picture of the consistency of such policies throughout the years of Soviet rule. The evidence seems to indicate that invasions into scientific matters have been sporadic rather than constant. If so, Soviet scientists may have been able to work in relative freedom for long periods, being compelled to run for the storm cellars only once in a decade when the Party theoreticians chose to turn their attention again to the ideological purity of scientific work.

Nor do we know anything about the manner and degree of official control over the determination of scientific research programs. The far-from-conclusive evidence suggests that

planning in the advanced or nebulous fields of science is not
rigid and is perhaps not effective. Many Soviet scientists still
seem to retain a substantial degree of autonomy in the selection and pursuit of their own research projects.

Nevertheless, there are some data that cast light on the
attitude of Soviet officials toward nuclear research. This attitude was the result of two basically contradictory views about
science that governed the actions of the Bolshevik leaders in
the early years of Soviet rule: One view was that there is
an irreconcilable conflict between "pure" and "applied" research, and that the former has no place in the Soviet system.
The other was that the doctrine of dialectical materialism—
so important a foundation of the Soviet system—would be
borne out and thus strengthened by the findings of research
in all fields of science. The contradiction between these views
arises from the fact that the philosophical implications of
scientific research are to be found mainly by the free method
of inquiry, which the Bolsheviks labeled "pure."

The first view required that every activity within the
Soviet Union be consciously directed toward building the
new communist society. This requirement led Soviet leaders
to insist that scientists discard the tradition of "pure academism" and "unite theory and practice." They urged scientists to pursue only those problems that promised a quick
payoff for Soviet industry. This led to a clash with many
scientists. It created between the Soviet government and the
Academy of Sciences an estrangement that continued for
more than a decade after the revolution. Clinging to tradi-
tions that reached back two hundred years in Russian history, the Academy was the nest of the "pure academism" so
despised by the Soviet government. Not until 1929 was political coordination of the Academy of Sciences begun with
the admission of Communist Party members as scholars of
the Academy. At the same time, the Soviet authorities were

able to get the Academy to accommodate some of its research programs to the needs of the industrialization called for by the first Five-Year Plan in 1928. In 1935 a Technical Sciences Section was attached to the Academy. Before that, the Academy had had control only over research in the humanities; research in the exact sciences was conducted in the industrial commissariats.

The *rapprochement* between government and science was also reflected in administrative measures. In 1934, the Academy was moved from Leningrad to Moscow and placed under the jurisdiction of the Council of Peoples' Commissars. Its membership was enlarged to receive, along with practitioners of applied science, more party members than it had included between 1929 (when the first were admitted) and 1934.

The Academy of Sciences was obviously being brought into the communist fold; clearly it no longer made its own house rules. The changing scene was perhaps reflected in a toast to science given by Stalin on May 17, 1938:

To the progress of science, that science which does not allow its old and recognized leaders to invest themselves smugly in the robe of pontiffs and monopolists of science, which understands the meaning, significance, and omnipotence of and alliance between the old scientists and the young scientists, which voluntarily and readily opens all the doors of science to the young forces of our country and gives them the opportunity of scaling the summits of science, which recognizes that the future belongs to the young scientists.[7]

Nuclear physics was particularly susceptible to becoming the object of intellectual curiosity on the part of Bolshevik politicians. For, according to Communist legend, Engels was the father of modern atomic theory. The *Great Soviet Encyclopedia* claims:

The concept of the atom as a qualitatively peculiar material system possessing distinct individuality and at the same time as something changeable and free to transmute itself was formulated by F. Engels and further developed by V. I. Lenin. The idealists denied even the existence of material atoms. The development of modern physics has fully confirmed the concept of dialectical materialism about the atom.

It might have been expected, therefore, that the politicians would be looking with special interest over the shoulders of the nuclear physicists. Bolshevik "philosophers" insisted that explanations of the behavior of atomic particles be in accordance with the principles of Marx and Engels. The most distinguished physicists felt compelled to pay obeisance to the genius of Stalin and the virtues of the Soviet system. Some physicists, such as the brilliant Landau, were actually arrested by the NKVD for lapses from orthodoxy (though they were later released).

If political difficulties of this kind had been heavy and frequent, or if the Soviet government had insisted that nuclear research be supported only if there was solid assurance of its making a concrete contribution to the state, Soviet nuclear physics might not have grown as vigorously as it did. The fact that it did may indicate that it had a modicum of protection from political hazards.

Some protection may have been afforded by the fact that during the early thirties nuclear research was being carried on within the administrative orbit of the People's Commissariat of Heavy Industry (NKTP). Since this ministry was responsible for highly practical economic problems, some "pure" research could have led a sheltered existence within it, escaping the notice of those Bolsheviks who wanted to wield the ax against any activity that did not promise an early payoff. Such research was further nourished by N. I. Bukharin, who was for a while director of the Scientific Sector of the NKTP. Bukharin was a leading theoretician of the Communist Party and, as an intellectual, would have been more inclined than some of his fellow Bolsheviks to understand the point of view of scientists even though he might not always agree with them. In any event, the theoretical, as opposed to the practical, aspects of communism would have been less in conflict with the ideals of scientists on the so-called issue of pure *versus* applied science. One tenet of dialectical materialism, of which Bukharin was then the recognized high priest, held that there was no pure science, that all science was applied, because some of its findings were used sooner, some later. This view resolved the "contradiction" between pure and applied science that practical-minded Bolsheviks were using as an argument to force scientists into the service of the state.

Bukharin had a keen personal interest in science. A former Soviet physicist now in the United States refers to him as the "Vannevar Bush of Soviet science." Indeed, Bukharin may have had a special interest in nuclear physics. He showed such interest on one occasion in 1927 when he attended a lecture by George Gamow on thermonuclear reactions in the sun and offered to make available to Gamow the entire electrical power of Leningrad, if it were feasible to set off a thermonuclear reaction in the manner described in the lecture. The method described by Gamow called for sending large quantities of electric current through a thick wire in order to burst it at high temperature and thereby effect thermonuclear reactions similar to those occurring in the sun and stars. All of this may have led Bukharin to be sympathetic toward the beginnings of Soviet nuclear research. The fact that Soviet nuclear science did not begin under the auspices of the Academy of Sciences was perhaps also fortunate—at least as far as its future was concerned; for the Academy was not in good standing at the time, and it had no section devoted to the supervision of the exact sciences. Possibly nuclear physicists were better off in the 1920's and early 1930's being under the wing of an approved ministry rather than under that of a distrusted and neglected scientific institution.

By the time nuclear research was transferred to the Academy of Sciences in 1938 or 1939, the Academy enjoyed the favor of the government. In 1938 Bukharin was liquidated and the large network of scientific institutions was gradually assimilated into the Academy. The time for the shift of atomic research to the Academy was particularly propitious because it coincided with the discovery of fission by Hahn and Strassmann in Germany in December 1938, a discovery that enhanced considerably the prospects for man-released atomic energy. Thenceforth this increasingly important scientific activity was watched over by an institution that was no longer out of favor with the government and that included many who preserved the spirit of free scientific inquiry.

Though the program of the Academy was in theory tightly controlled by the central government, it had grown to such tremendous size that Soviet bureaucrats could not keep watch over every research project. This probably permitted officials of the Academy a certain amount of latitude and may have made it possible for nuclear research to receive rather lavish support without the knowledge of high Soviet officials; for many of the Soviet actions regarding atomic energy in the prewar period suggest that the political authorities were actually not informed about the nature or importance of their own already well-oriented nuclear research program.

2

THE EARLY SCIENTIFIC BASE

The foremost factor in any scientific program is a competent, imaginative cadre. By the middle thirties there were able, active, and enthusiastic groups of young nuclear physicists in several institutes in the USSR. Leningrad was the major center. And Ioffe's own Physico-Technical Institute in that city was the most active in nuclear research. Important work was also being done at the Radium Institute in Leningrad, at the Lebedev Physical Institute and the Institute of Physical Problems in Moscow, and at Kharkov's Physico-Technical Institute.

Ioffe's major role in establishing this scientific complex is indicated by the homage paid him by other Soviet physicists on the occasion of his sixtieth birthday, in 1940:

For us Soviet physicists . . . Professor A. F. Ioffe is not only a great scientist, he is also honored by us as the founder and organizer of modern physics in the Soviet Union. . . . Most of the major physical researches which are being conducted in the Soviet Union, concerning the mechanical, electrical, and magnetic properties of solid bodies, X-rays, electronic processes, the physics of atomic nuclei—in short all the fundamental problems outside of optics, radiophysics, and chemical physics—have been initiated by A. F. Ioffe and have been advanced by him or, under his guidance, by his numerous pupils and their pupils. The development of this army of young Soviet physicists, which at the present time is many hundreds, can also be traced ultimately to Ioffe's initiative, energy, and foresight.[1]

Outstanding among the atomic scientists in these and related institutes were Lev D. Landau, Yakov I. Frenkel, Yulii B. Khariton, Kyrill D. Sinel'nikov, Sergei L. Sobolev, and Igor Vasilevich Kurchatov.

Landau, an ideological maverick, was perhaps the most brilliant theoretician of them all. His work encompassed almost all the advanced frontiers of nuclear physics. Frenkel, a versatile theorist, formulated a theory of fission at approximately the same time that Bohr and Wheeler produced similar findings in the West. Frenkel died in 1952, in the midst of a barrage of ideological attacks. Khariton, who had studied at Cambridge when Kapitsa was there, combined experimental and theoretical skills. Along with Zeldovich, he made important early contributions to the theory of the nuclear chain reaction. Sinel'nikov, also a former student at Cambridge, was a brilliant experimentalist who later became the director of the Kharkov Physico-Technical Institute. At the present time he is directing important nuclear reactor research near Moscow.

S. L. Sobolev, an outstanding mathematician, was hailed as a man of "the Stalin Breed." He was the youngest member of the Academy of Sciences at the time of his admission (as a corresponding member in 1933, a full member in 1939), and he appears to have aroused the jealousy of many of his colleagues. In 1945 he held an important administrative position in Kurchatov's laboratory, at the very center of the Soviet Union's atomic energy program, and he has since made significant contributions toward the development of the complex calculation techniques and machines used in connection with atomic energy.

Mention must also be made of the Soviet state's first Nobel prize winners. In the field of chemical kinetics, Nikolai N. Semenov is the outstanding personality. His work in chain reactions is applicable to the nuclear chain reaction. Indeed, the work of Khariton and Zeldovich was performed under Semenov's direction at his Institute of Chemical Physics.

In 1934, the late Sergei Vavilov was directing the research of a young physicist, Pavel Cherenkov, in the relationship of certain types of nuclear radiation to luminescence. Cherenkov unexpectedly found that pure water became faintly luminescent when traversed by gamma rays. This discovery and its theoretical interpretations by Ilya M. Frank and Igor E. Tamm won the trio the 1958 Nobel award. And in every nuclear research reactor of the water type one can see Cherenkov's "blue glow."

The most important of all the Soviet atomic scientists from the very beginning of Soviet nuclear research to the present time is Igor Vasilevich Kurchatov. In 1938, at the age of thirty-five, he was director of the Nuclear Physics Laboratory at the Leningrad Physico-Technical Institute; and he has headed the major USSR research efforts since. He is the only person given public credit in the *Great Soviet Encyclopedia* for the USSR atomic energy program; this is the strongest possible acclaim.

Kurchatov had worked at the Institute since 1925 on nonnuclear research. But the beginning of the thirties marked a new period of intense excitement and discovery in the small enclaves of nuclear researchers in Cambridge, Copenhagen, and Rome. Kurchatov's brother-in-law, K. D. Sinel'nikov, had just returned from Lord Rutherford's Cavendish Laboratory and spoke enthusiastically of nuclear physics. And in 1932, on the banks of the Neva at Leningrad, Kurchatov and colleagues Skobel'tsyn, Alikhanov, and Artzimovich held spirited discussions with Frédéric Joliot-Curie of France about the problems of nuclear physics. Shortly thereafter the same discussants were active in the All-Union Conference on the Atomic Nucleus at Leningrad, and by then Kurchatov was determinedly entrenched in his nuclear research tasks.

Mainly repeating, verifying, and extending nuclear experiments done elsewhere, especially those of Enrico Fermi at Rome, Kurchatov's group also accomplished some significant original work. Thus, by the later thirties, Kurchatov had acquired considerable status and recognition, at least in the USSR, particularly for his investigations in the field of nuclear isomerism.

As distinguished from "isotopes"—which are members of the same chemical element with identical atomic numbers but with different atomic weights—"isomers" are nuclei of the same chemical element with identical atomic weights, differing only in mode or rate of radioactive decay. The first set of *naturally* occurring isomers was discovered in 1921 by Otto Hahn, later co-discoverer of the processes of fission. In January 1934, Joliot-Curie and his wife announced the artificial creation of radioactive elements (for which they received the Nobel prize). Following this, in 1935, Igor Kurchatov, directing a group that included his brother Boris, discovered the first instance of isomerism in an *artificially* radioactive element. In fact, Kurchatov's work is so interwoven in the fabric of early nuclear research and with the names of others far famed that his relative anonymity in the West, until 1955, is somewhat paradoxical.

Peter L. Kapitsa, the "Atom-Czar" of the Western press,

was not among those most actively engaged in Soviet nuclear research. When he was in political favor, he filled the role of senior statesman, committee member, and adviser in atomic physics, a role for which he was well fitted because of his broad interests, his forceful personality, and his position as director of the Moscow Institute of Physical Problems. But, contrary to widely held opinion in the West, he was not in charge of the Soviet atomic project.

The men we have been discussing worked in laboratories having equipment that compared favorably with the laboratory equipment of most other major nations in the thirties. By the end of the thirties and the beginning of the forties, Soviet scientists were using the cyclotron, the classical "atom smasher," in atomic research. In this respect they were better off than any of their European counterparts and not much worse off than American scientists. Considering the expense of these machines, and the length of time needed to design and construct them, their availability to Soviet scientists may indicate the degree of support enjoyed by nuclear research in the USSR. Either the acquisition of this equipment taxed the ingenuity and persuasive powers of administrators of science such as Ioffe, or the Soviet government was taking an optimistic view of the potentialities of nuclear research at a surprisingly early date. Of course, the small cyclotron then in existence cost only a fraction as much as the large ones being built today. For purposes of comparison, the combined cost of the first two machines at Berkeley was probably no more than $1,000,000 in 1939 dollars.[2] Such figures do not loom large in the national budget of any country. But as a single item in a budget for scientific research[3] they would be likely to catch the attention of administrators and, in the Soviet Union especially, would probably be approved only if justified.

The Soviet Union's cyclotron at the Radium Institute in

Leningrad was the first one in Europe. It was ready for limited operation in 1937. Its beam energy was gradually increased in succeeding years, and it was fully equipped and in use for experimental work by the end of 1940 or the beginning of 1941. This machine was smaller than the 37-inch cyclotron then in operation at Berkeley, but published studies show that it was adequate for studying the fission process and for producing fission products. For example, a reference dating from the spring of 1941 indicates that this cyclotron was used to obtain radioactive iodine from the fission of thorium and uranium.

This small cyclotron was the only one in actual operation in the Soviet Union until the war stopped all atomic research. But two additional cyclotrons were either planned or under construction in 1940. One of these was assigned to the Physico-Technical Institute in Leningrad and was scheduled for completion by the spring of 1941. Its magnet weight and the electric power required to operate it were approximately half those of the large (60-inch) cyclotron that had been put into operation at Berkeley in 1939. While these specifications alone do not permit a precise comparison, it would appear that the second Soviet cyclotron was designed to achieve a capability comparable to (though somewhat less than) that of the larger Berkeley machine, which was, at that time, the world's largest. The third Soviet cyclotron, scheduled for construction in 1941 and for installation in the Lebedev Physical Institute at Moscow, represented a leap into the big leagues. Its design was under the direction of D. V. Skobel'tsyn, who became director of the Laboratory of the Atomic Nucleus of the Lebedev Institute in 1941, and who, since the war, has represented the Soviet Union at the United Nations and at other international conferences on matters relating to atomic energy. Skobel'tsyn is now director of the entire Lebedev Institute.

This machine was designed to produce a deuteron beam of 50 million electron volts, strong enough "for obtaining artificial radioactive elements in great quantities." Such energy was approximately three times greater than that obtainable by the 60-inch cyclotron at Berkeley. (Berkeley, at that time, was constructing its 184-inch cyclotron, which, however, was not completed until after World War II.)

The war interrupted construction of the Leningrad cyclotron, and apparently caused the Moscow cyclotron to be abandoned while it was still in the planning stage. The Leningrad cyclotron appeared to be in the same advanced stage of construction as the Berkeley machine when construction was halted. The abandoned magnet of the Leningrad cyclotron was rusting away in the Electrosila factory until late 1944, when work on it was resumed, with completion scheduled for December 1945. But newly discovered principles of acceleration rendered the original design obsolete, and construction plans were probably modified accordingly.

The second and third Soviet cyclotrons, then, were victims of the war. But, even in the planning stage, they symbolize the high level that atomic research had reached in the USSR by the end of the 1930's. The design of both machines demonstrated that in theoretical ideas and in knowledge of experimental techniques Soviet scientists were equal to their counterparts in the West. And the plan to build them indicated that the Russians were interested in providing their scientists with equipment with which they could perform independent work on the atomic nucleus. With such laboratory equipment in institutions well disposed toward nuclear research, Soviet physicists were adequately prepared to exploit the discovery of nuclear fission when it occurred in Germany in 1938. At last, here was a potential energy source of great significance to the Soviet state, if it could be utilized.

Within five months of Hahn and Strassmann's fundamental discovery, Soviet scientists made a finding that contributed to uncovering the essential link between fission and
the chain reaction, an achievement that can be best understood only from the perspective of the world's understanding
of fission at the beginning of 1939.

The discovery that a neutron could split the uranium
atom and thereby release a tremendous amount of energy did
not in itself promise a practical source of nuclear power. At
a scientific conference in Washington, D.C., on January 26,
1939, the utilization of the fission phenomenon as a possible
source of nuclear power was first discussed "in a semi-jocular
earnest." Enrico Fermi suggested that several new neutrons
might be emitted during the fission process, thus providing
a mechanism that might propagate a chain reaction in a
uranium mass. Whether large amounts of energy could be
obtained by "burning" uranium depended on the number
of neutrons set free in the process of fission. Many experiments were undertaken throughout the world to determine
this and other characteristics of the fission process. Several
groups in the United States and a group headed by Joliot-
Curie in France concluded that fission neutrons were rather
abundant. On the basis of an entirely independent experiment, two of Kurchatov's workers, Rusinov and Flerov, reported at a neutron seminar at the Leningrad Physico-
Technical Institute in April 1939 that between two and four
neutrons were emitted per fissioned nucleus. Since this was
a quantity sufficient to guarantee the continuous reproduction of nuclear energy, Rusinov and Flerov concluded that
a chain reaction now seemed possible.

Other Soviet scientists were also working on chain reaction. In consultation with Kurchatov, Y. B. Zeldovich
and Y. B. Khariton of the Institute of Chemical Physics (now
at Moscow, but then at Leningrad) initiated a series of theo-

retical studies on chain reaction (both slow and explosive). Their initial studies were published late in 1939, after being reported at a conference on the atomic nucleus held at Kharkov.

Two important extensions of their work were published in 1940. One of these dealt mainly with the requirements for creating explosive conditions in a critical mass of fissionable material, which indicates that Soviet scientists should have been no less aware of the possible military usefulness of atomic energy than were scientists in the Western world.

During November 15–20, 1939, the Conference on Questions of the Physics of the Atomic Nucleus was held at Kharkov. The reports of that meeting make it clear that, at the time, the state of the new art in the Soviet Union was understood and appreciated as it was in the West. For example, among the studies reported were those of Zeldovich and Khariton on the theory of chain reactions, which were published later the same year. The conference papers also indicated that Soviet researchers were fully informed about theoretical and experimental developments in the West; they were replete with references to work published abroad. The classic work of Zeldovich and Khariton and the proceedings of the Kharkov conference were not available to scientists of the U.S. Manhattan Project in translated form until 1945.[4]

Suggestions of Official Interest in Nuclear Research

The calling of this meeting was in itself an indication that Soviet interest in the subject of nuclear energy was widespread and active, as was also the creation, in the spring of 1940, of the Special Committee for the Problem of Uranium. This committee was set up under the Presidium of the Academy of Sciences, the highest and most authoritative administrative level to which any scientific problem in the Soviet Union could be referred. The Special Committee included some of the most distinguished scientists in the Soviet Union. Its chairman was V. G. Khlopin, who had succeeded Vernadskii as head of the Radium Institute. The other members, as listed in the decree setting up the committee, were:

Academicians:
>V. I. Vernadskii
>A. F. Ioffe
>A. Y. Fersman
>S. I. Vavilov
>P. I. Lazarev
>A. N. Frumkin
>L. I. Mandel'stam
>G. M. Krzhizhanovskii
>P. L. Kapitsa

Professors:
>I. V. Kurchatov
>D. I. Shcherbakov
>A. P. Vinogradov
>Y. B. Khariton

The relative status or importance of a person in a particular activity is indicated by the sequence of names. It is interesting to note that Kapitsa was the last of the academicians listed and there is no reason to believe that his later role in the atomic energy program was ever enhanced. Kurchatov, not yet an academician, was the top professor in the program. Elected to the Academy in 1943, Kurchatov's name would then have appeared at the top of any similar commission.

The duties assigned to this committee indicate that the Academy of Sciences had in mind a comprehensive and well-organized pursuit of all aspects of the problem, from prospecting for ore to constructing cyclotrons. The following "tasks" were listed in the decree:

1. To prepare a scientific research program for the study of uranium, and to assign various parts of it to the institutes of the Academy of Sciences;

2. To organize the development of methods for separating the fissionable uranium isotope, and pursue research on controlling the processes of radioactive disintegration (that is, controlling a chain reaction);

3. To coordinate and exercise general supervision over scientific research projects of the Academy of Sciences on the problem of uranium.

A second conference on radioactivity was also scheduled at the Radium Institute for 1941.

In the same decree, the Presidium of the Academy of Sciences recognized "the necessity of using powerful cyclotrons for work on the problem of uranium," and gave specific orders:

1. That the Radium Institute cyclotron, then already in operation, be "completely equipped" by the end of 1940;

2. That construction of the Physico-Technical Institute's cyclotron be completed "not later than the first quarter of 1941";

3. That the Lebedev Physical Institute in Moscow prepare by October 15, 1940, the design and construction plan for a "new, powerful cyclotron in Moscow," to be included in the Academy budget for capital construction for 1941.

The Presidium of the Academy of Sciences also gave attention to the problem of acquiring raw materials. It set up a State Fund for Uranium Metal and organized a special expedition to prospect for uranium. The distinguished geologist A. Y. Fersman was to be the leader of the expedition. The prospecting was to be done during 1940, and the group was to study "the more important deposits of uranium in Central Asia." Fersman's group was also instructed to call a special conference at Tashkent, in collaboration with the Uzbek branch of the Academy of Sciences, to study problems

of uranium prospecting and to submit to the Presidium a
"project for action" for the newly created State Fund for
Uranium Metal.

This concern with uranium deposits obviously indicated
an intention to carry on an intensive collection of the raw
materials necessary for an atomic program of significant
dimensions. It is unlikely that mere scientific interest in the
geology of uranium deposits prompted this activity, because
such inquiry was not new. Fersman had led expeditions in
search of uranium more than a decade earlier. Throughout
1939, before the Presidium's decree, there were numerous
references in Soviet chemical and geological journals to the
exploration of deposits and the extraction of uranium ores.
The decree of 1940 reflected, rather, a determination to
obtain ore in quantities sufficient for purposes other than
simply small-scale scientific inquiry. It is interesting to note
that discussion in the United States on the problem of obtaining large quantities of uranium ore from the Belgian
Congo began at about this same time, on June 1, 1940. What
is more, the recognition given in this decree to the necessity
of separating uranium isotopes was almost simultaneous with
a similar decision reached at a meeting of the U.S. Uranium
Committee on April 28, 1940. Finally, the reference to the
creation of the State Fund for Uranium Metal, which was
not mentioned again in Soviet publications, can mean only
that the Soviet Union began accumulating uranium in 1940
for purposes other than conventional industrial uses (such
as ceramics and certain steel alloys, for which uranium had
long been used). The contemplated rate of extraction in
those early years was probably great enough to provide metallic uranium for a large-scale experimental program.

Another event occurred in the spring of 1940 indicating
that serious attention at a high level was being paid to practical work in nuclear energy. On April 16–17, 1940, the first

All-Union Conference on Isotopes was called by the Commission for Isotopes of the Academy of Sciences. Many papers were presented at this conference on the production—including the "industrial" production—of heavy water, which is used as a moderator, or slowing-down substance, for neutrons in the chain reaction. Plans were discussed for producing heavy water by electrolysis at the rate of 15 kilograms (33 lb.) per year in a factory at the city of Chirchik, near Tashkent, in Central Asia. This amount would have been insignificant for building a nuclear reactor, but quite adequate for a heavy experimental program short of an actual test reactor. Also discussed was the separation of uranium isotopes by both the mass spectrograph and the thermal diffusion of uranium hexafluoride.

The Commission for Isotopes was created in 1939, with V. I. Vernadskii as its director. The All-Union Conference was the first conference called under its auspices and was probably also the last to convene publicly. At this meeting a second conference was scheduled by resolution for July 1941. But the literature for 1941 does not record that such a conference was held. Indeed, it is unlikely that a conference on atomic energy would have been convened under the conditions of war in 1941 and 1942.

There is further evidence that the year 1940 was a high point in the history of Soviet nuclear physics. Kurchatov and his collaborators and students were working rapidly and were on the verge of some exciting discoveries. They were beginning extensive radiochemical studies and counting experiments on the nature of the fission process; this work perhaps constituted the most important and fundamental Soviet contribution to the understanding of nuclear fission.

Conclusive proof of the spontaneous fission of uranium was one of the spectacular accomplishments of the year. It was established by two of Kurchatov's students, Konstantin

A. Petrzhak and Georgii N. Flerov, under Kurchatov's supervision. A few months later, I. S. Panasyuk and Flerov established the existence of the same phenomenon in thorium.

The Russians are justified in claiming priority for the
discovery of spontaneous fission. In May 1939, W. F. Libby,*
at the University of California, had used two different
methods to find evidence of spontaneous fission in uranium
and thorium, but without success. Petrzhak and Flerov
achieved their success by counting the pulses of fission products, a method different from those tried by Libby. Their
work showed an ingenuity and meticulousness usually expected from a fine Western laboratory.

As mentioned previously, Flerov had performed (with
Rusinov) one of the earliest experiments on the number of
neutrons emitted per fission. Later these two worked on the
resonance absorption of neutrons in uranium-238, a phenomenon that leads to the formation of neptunium and plutonium (although the formation of the latter element was
not clear at the time). At a neutron seminar at Leningrad
in the spring of 1940, Flerov and Petrzhak reported on the
minimum energy of neutrons required to fission U-238 and
thorium-232. This and other fine work has led to Flerov's
being regarded as one of the Soviet Union's top experimental
nuclear physicists.

In November 1940, another Conference on the Physics of
Atomic Nuclei was called, this time at Moscow. The proceedings of this conference reveal that a considerable body
of data, of both Western and Soviet origin, had been accu-
mulated and assimilated by the Soviet nuclear physicists.
They also show clearly that, at the end of the second year
of the era of fission, the Soviet Union was still not lagging

* Commissioner, U.S. Atomic Energy Commission, 1954–59.

behind the West in the understanding and appreciation of the potential uses of the fission process.

The increasing tempo of Soviet nuclear development continued until June 1941. Soviet scientific literature shows that the program established in the previous year by the Uranium Committee was being energetically carried out during the first six months of 1941.

Important experimental work by individual scientists was also in progress during this time. For example, N. A. Perfilov of the Radium Institute began to develop new techniques for obtaining various nuclear constants of uranium involving the use of the Wilson cloud chamber, photo-emulsions, and magnetic fields. These experiments, which presumably were dropped during the first phases of the war, were resumed later, and some of the results were published between 1944 and 1946.

Probably the most significant developments in the spring of 1941 were directed toward the discovery of methods for quantity production of the critical materials for fission, namely, U-235 and heavy water. At the Radium Institute, Alkhazov and Murin were developing a method for separating uranium isotopes by linear acceleration of uranium ions. Calculations comparing this method with the mass spectrographic process (one of the major methods adopted in the United States) were in progress, and Alkhazov and Murin concluded that their method would be much the more effective one. Their published findings indicate an intensive interest in eventually separating U-235 on a large scale.

The problem of separating uranium isotopes was being studied at about the same rate in the United States and the USSR, except that in the theoretical exploration of some of these methods the Russians may have been somewhat in the lead. For example, the methods of the mass spectrograph

and the thermal diffusion of uranium hexafluoride were discussed in the USSR in April 1940, while the first serious
suggestion of the use of thermal diffusion of uranium hexafluoride was made in the United States in September 1940.
And while papers on the production of heavy water on an
industrial scale were presented in the Soviet Union in April
1940, it was not until nearly a year later, in February 1941,
that the first work, directed toward large-scale production,
was done in the United States, at Columbia University.
Finally, research related to a process for producing heavy
water by "the exchange reaction between deuterium and
hydrogen on nickel" was reported early in 1941 by S. Levina
of the Karpov Institute at Moscow (in one of several papers
relating to this problem); this same process was used at the
Consolidated Mining and Smelting Company at Trail, British Columbia, for the Manhattan Project, beginning about
1943 and continuing for a number of years thereafter.

In general, therefore, it would appear that the Soviet
Union and the United States were progressing toward important achievements in nuclear physics at about an equal
pace.

3

THE WAR CALLS A
HALT

June 1941 brought an end to this parallel development. The exigencies of war led to diametrically opposed decisions: for the United States and Britain a sharply accelerated program; for the Russians an almost total halt.[1]

The impact of the German military attack on the Soviet nuclear energy program is clearly revealed in the Soviet scientific literature of 1941 and 1942. After the attack, the Leningrad Physico-Technical Institute quickly swung over to problems of immediate urgency. Previously scheduled work was scrapped, and "all released forces were directed to . . . military problems . . . to the demands of the front."[2]

An editorial in *Leningrad Pravda* took up the cry on July 9, 1941:

In the interests of the front, the work of the numerous laboratories and institutes must be reoriented. In the polytechnical institutes and in the chairs of the universities the reorientation for war work has already begun. The scientific

worker and inventor must at the present time concentrate
on one idea—how he can hasten the destruction of the faith-
less enemy; in what way he can help the Red Army, the Red
Fleet. Now, the scientists of our Motherland must work for
the front, and only for the front!

The leader of the Soviet nuclear research effort, I. V.
Kurchatov, dropped his work on the new Leningrad cyclotron and was dispatched to the Black Sea to work on the
problem of protecting ships from German mines, work for
which he received a Stalin prize in January 1942. And as the
German armies advanced deep into European Russia, cap-
turing or threatening major towns, scientific institutions were
hastily evacuated and resettled in the east: at Kazan, Frunze,
Krasnoyarsk, Sverdlovsk, Miass, Ul'yanovsk, Tashkent, Yela-
buga, and Alma-Ata. Under such conditions, any work going
on in these institutes was bound to suffer. Dislocation and
disruption further reduced the scientific resources of the
USSR. Nevertheless, some work on radioactive isotopes and
cosmic rays seems to have continued during the period of
crisis between mid-1941 and 1943.

But, since there was no censorship on the subject of
atomic energy, the meagerness of information probably indicates that the work, even in these restricted fields, was on a
very small scale. What it consisted of is revealed in part in
a report on the work of the Radium Institute given by its
director, Vitalii G. Khlopin, in October 1941. He said that
"almost all the projects on which the Institute is working
are new" and that the nuclear physicists of the Radium Institute were engaged in such matters as diagnosis in military
medicine by means of radioisotopes and developing methods
of examination of industrial materials by means of gamma
rays. It may have been such projects to which Ioffe referred
when he said, in November 1942: "From the scientists' en-

deavors to devote all their knowledge to the tasks of defense, ingenious instruments came into being, where most precise methods of the physics of the atomic nucleus were used to solve concrete problems of war or production."[3]

Neither Khlopin nor Ioffe suggested the scope of this practical utilization of atomic energy, although in the prewar period a number of scientists had displayed considerable interest in the field. In the wartime publications, references to concrete applications of radioisotopes in industry or medicine are rare. Certainly, the quantity of artificial radioisotopes in the Soviet Union must have been very small. The Radium Institute cyclotron was too small to produce them in quantity, and by 1941 the Russians could not possibly have had in operation a reactor capable of producing them. Presumably, therefore, the practice was on a small, perhaps only experimental, scale.

It may be possible to speculate also that Ioffe's remark may have been in some way related to the peculiar fact that, while almost all Soviet nuclear physicists whose wartime activity can be traced (and this applies to most of them) were working on projects directly related to the war and unrelated to nuclear physics, some cosmic-ray specialists continued to work in their field without interruption throughout the war. For example, early in 1945 Alikhanov and Alikhanian published the results of investigations they had conducted in Armenia (on Mount Alagez and at Erevan) during 1942, 1943, and 1944. There are few subjects in physics more remote from concrete application than cosmic-ray research. Perhaps the possibility should not be dismissed, however, that the Russians hoped to find it in some way useful.

None of this work, however, alters the fact that, following the German attack, there was a virtually complete cessation of large-scale nuclear research in the Soviet Union.

On the surface it seems that the Western powers and the USSR were, in 1941, entering the payoff area of atomic development at an equal pace. In the main, both efforts had arrived at similar results at very nearly the same time. It might appear that the Russians had been running neck and neck with the Americans and British in a race to find avenues for releasing atomic energy.

The meaning of the parallel development, until the war interfered, of the Soviet and Western atomic research programs can be distorted if viewed against the background of the race for nuclear weapons in the postwar period. The Russians may in fact have considered themselves in a race with the Western world during the period 1930–41, but it does not necessarily follow that the goal they had in mind was an atomic bomb. The nearly simultaneous discoveries in the USSR and in the West, and the apparently parallel rise in scientific competence, may have been caused in part by the nonpolitical competition in which scientists in all countries often engage. Many of the advances may have come at roughly the same time simply because nuclear science had reached the same level of growth in both the Soviet Union and the West. A race for atomic weapons could have occurred only if the governments concerned had decided on large-scale production programs. Neither the Anglo-Americans nor, so far as the available evidence shows, the USSR had made such a decision by the middle of 1941. Contrary to rather commonly held opinion in the United States, the American and British decisions to launch a large-scale, governmentally sponsored development and production project were reached neither easily nor quickly. The final decision to engage in an energetic program was not made by the United States until the end of November 1941, after nearly two years of painstaking inquiry and difficult deliberation. And by the time the Americans and the British did decide on a nuclear weapons program, the Soviet Union had been forced by circumstances beyond its control to stop or postpone its atomic research program.

Moreover, it appears that governmental awareness of the military implications of atomic energy was more backward in the Soviet Union than in the West, though this can by no means be established beyond question. By the end of 1939 and the spring of 1940, respectively, the American and British governments had set up official committees of experts to study the potentialities of atomic energy for military purposes. There is no trace in prewar Soviet publications of any similar action by the Soviet government. The Uranium Committee established in April 1940 by the Soviet Academy of Sciences bears no resemblance—judging by the published information about its duties—to the Thomson Committee of Great Britain or the Jewett Committee of the United States. The Thomson Committee was set up in Great Britain in April 1940 and was instructed "to report as soon as possible whether the possibilities of producing atomic bombs during this war, and their military effect, were sufficient to justify the necessary diversion of effort for this purpose."[4] The Jewett Committee was set up in the spring of 1941 "to evaluate the military importance of the uranium problem and to recommend the level of expenditure at which the problem should be investigated."[5]

The existence of the latter two committees, however, was secret at the time, and if there had been a counterpart in the USSR, it would also no doubt have been kept from public notice. Moreover, the Russians would not have been likely to publish such information even later, because they are in general less prone than Westerners to declassify outdated security information; if there were military secrets hidden in the early history of Soviet atomic research and development, they are still locked up in the Kremlin's archives.

However, if an examination of the military potential of atomic energy had been ordered by the Soviet political authorities, the Soviet censor would certainly have placed an over-all ban on publication of data about atomic energy. As soon as military considerations entered the thinking of Western atomic scientists, a curtain of secrecy was drawn over the subject. Soviet security policy in general is even more strict and thorough than that of the West; yet the Soviet press continued to discuss atomic energy until 1943, when the Russians resumed a nuclear energy program. This argues against the possibility that the Russians had a counterpart of the Thomson and Jewett committees.

Given the state of knowledge of Soviet nuclear physicists, it is almost impossible to believe that any similar Soviet committee could have reached conclusions different from those reached in the latter part of 1941 in Britain and the United States. Further, it is highly improbable that Soviet policy-makers were so sophisticated about atomic energy that they examined the question of its military potential months before the British and Americans did and arrived at a conclusion contrary to that reached by the latter. There is a good deal of evidence, on the other hand, that the Soviet political leaders did not become fully aware of the military aspects of nuclear energy until it was too late for them to transform their large-scale research effort into a development and production program.

4

MOTIVATION

If the Soviet government in fact was not aware of, or did not take seriously, the possible military utility of atomic energy, it may be worth while to try to show how it was that nuclear research could have reached the high level that it did in the Soviet Union by 1941—especially since we are dealing with a totalitarian state where theoretically (and actually in most fields) all activity is planned and controlled by central political authorities. Moreover, we should try to account for such apparent specific indicators of government interest as the ready approval given to Ioffe by Ordzhonikidze for an appropriation for nuclear research, the special interest in radioactive ores, and the rather large investment in cyclotrons.

It is necessary to guard against errors in interpretation of data about early Soviet work on nuclear physics caused by projecting current knowledge backward to a time when there was general skepticism about the possibility of releasing and

controlling atomic energy. For example, some data about
Soviet uranium prospecting in 1929 and 1930 could be so
misinterpreted. In those years, Soviet authorities revealed
a special interest in uranium-bearing pegmatite ores found
by geologists. An air of secrecy surrounded the subject, and
geological reports were often censored before publication
to remove references to pegmatite ores. Someone, in other
words, was taking a serious view of uranium ores and was,
for some reason, trying to keep the matter under security
wraps. Today, in the light of the intense interest in uranium
ore since 1945, one might leap to the conclusion that as early
as 1929 the Soviet government wanted to acquire uranium
ore for use in a large-scale nuclear research program. This
conclusion would be anachronistic and therefore erroneous.
The early interest in radioactive materials was probably
partly the result of widespread and exaggerated enthusiasm
over the healing properties of radioactive materials and
partly due to the great value of these substances; Soviet
interest in accumulating gold and rare metals has always
been high, and it is known that Stalin took a personal interest in radioactive minerals.

But the active and many-faceted atomic research program
during 1939–41 may have been carried on by the Academy
of Sciences without a full understanding on the part of Soviet
political leaders of its potential significance for military purposes. The Academy directs a vast research program in all
fields of science, and presumably the practical significance
of many aspects of it would ordinarily come to the attention
of political leaders only if scientists volunteered the information. As late as 1941 the Soviet government seemed unconcerned about the military potential of atomic energy; this
indifference may have been due merely to the Soviet scientists' failure to urge their political authorities to give official
attention to the matter, as Fermi and others did in the United

States. For that matter, the Soviet scientists themselves may not have foreseen the military possibilities of atomic energy as early as the American scientists did.

Yet the men in the Kremlin no doubt read their own newspapers, which carried fairly frequent articles on the subject of atomic energy. While these, apparently, discussed only the industrial possibilities of nuclear energy, even a nonscientist of average intelligence might have perceived some possibility that this energy might be applied directly to military ends. Given an efficient political process, a politician whose curiosity might have been aroused in this way could have been expected to call in scientists and ask their advice about the prospects for military use of atomic energy. But all government officials inevitably let some matters slip, particularly when they are harried by problems arising in periods as tense as the years 1939–41. It is not unreasonable to speculate that atomic energy was one of these matters that accidentally escaped careful attention by Soviet political leaders in the prewar years. War was raging in Europe. Germany was increasing its strength at a fearsome rate and was winning spectacular victories. After the middle of 1940, the Nazi-Soviet agreement was at best uneasy, and the possibility grew that Hitler might turn the *Wehrmacht* eastward. The Soviet Union was strenuously mobilizing its economy for war.

Given the poverty of Soviet industrial resources by comparison with the magnitude of the economic effort that was required, it might be argued that continuation of a large atomic research program would have been considered a luxury if the authorities really expected no significant short-run payoff. Yet, impressive as the Soviet atomic research program was, it clearly did not represent a serious diversion of resources from the armaments program; it was not cut back until the German attack actually occurred. The largest items of expenditure were the cyclotrons, especially the one scheduled for completion in 1941. The rest of the program was probably a relatively inconspicuous drain on the economy. Most of it could have been carried out with buildings and equipment already in being before the economic mobilization began. In the United States, for example, an atomic research program comparable to the Soviet one received only about $300,000 from the U.S. government between 1939 and the end of 1941; moreover, most of this amount was not allocated until the latter part of the period, and not all of it had been spent by the end of 1941. Since the cost was so small, then, the Soviet program may have been allowed to continue without interruption until June 1941, even without official awareness that nuclear energy might have had military implications.

Most of the recorded behavior of Soviet authorities in the period leading up to Nazi-Soviet hostilities can best be explained by assuming that they actually did not understand the military implications of atomic energy. They may even have been unaware that the American and British governments were much concerned about the subject.[1] If this is true, the parallel progress of the Soviet and Western atomic research programs in the period 1939–41 was not the result of competition for a breakthrough in the field of atomic weapons. By this reasoning, the Russians did not consciously enter the nuclear armaments race until later in the war, although when they did they started from the high plateau they had reached before the war began.

The question then becomes: When and how did the Russians become interested in developing the nuclear weapons? A detailed answer to this question is beyond the scope of this study. A rather striking indication of aroused interest occurred in the autumn of 1941. Peter Kapitsa addressed a meeting of scientists on October 12, 1941; the purpose of the meeting was to exhort scientists to devote their talents to winning the war. Discussing various ways in which scientists could help the war effort, Kapitsa said:

One of the basic weapons of modern warfare is explosive materials. Science demonstrates in principle that it is possible to increase their destructive force by one and one-half to two times. But recent years have seen the opening up of still newer possibilities—that is, the utilization of internal atomic energy. Theoretical calculations show that, whereas a modern high-explosive bomb can destroy an entire city block, an atom bomb, even one of small size, if it can be manufactured, could easily destroy a major capital city with several million inhabitants.

He prefaced this remark as follows:

I must admit that this [the problem of applying scientific research directly to defense against the Nazi attack] was quite new and unusual work for me, as until then it had never occurred to me that my knowledge could be used in the sphere of military technique. But a certain amount of experience which I have received in the last few months of work in this sphere has given rise in my mind to a number of ideas which I think may be of interest to you.

The general course of development of modern technology is roughly as follows. Scientific discoveries are gradually used in the solution of various technological problems, and this is the mainspring of technical progress. Consequently, it is inevitable that technology should to a certain extent lag behind the potentialities offered by the present level of science.

Strange as it may seem, this lag is most marked in the military sphere, perhaps chiefly because every new advance in military technique can only be properly tested in time of war, and must, moreover, be wielded by large numbers of men. Nevertheless, if we compare the last world war with the present one, we shall find that in those twenty years military technique has made big strides; and there can be no doubt that, with the present state of knowledge, these strides may be greater still.[2]

Kapitsa's awareness of the potentiality of nuclear energy for bombs seems to have been rather sudden. No doubt his realization could have been derived solely from the results of Soviet atomic research. But the timing of his statement is interesting: it was made only three months after the Thomson Committee reported to the Scientific Advisory Committee of the War Cabinet that the feasibility of a military weapon based on atomic energy had been definitely established and that this weapon had unprecedented powers of destruction, and less than one month before the Jewett Committee reported that an atom bomb was feasible and that its yield would be of the order of 300 tons of TNT per kilogram of uranium. There is no available evidence indicating that the Soviet espionage system could have conveyed the contents of these then-secret documents to Moscow as early as October 1941. But the possibility certainly exists. If Kapitsa's interest was actually stimulated by recently acquired knowledge about British and American estimates that atomic bombs were feasible, it is possible that the Thomson and Jewett reports were the turning points not only of the British and American atomic programs, but of the Soviet one as well.*

No Russian before Kapitsa, either scientist or government official, had ever linked atomic energy with an explosive weapon that might be useful in war. How widely his opinion was shared by Kapitsa's own colleagues is unknown. In another version of his speech, published several weeks later, the text was changed in a way that indicated a difference of opinion among Soviet scientists about the feasibility of constructing an atomic bomb. The alteration, however, could

---

* Kapitsa concluded his talk with an appeal for collaboration of foreign scientists with their Soviet colleagues. It is probable that Kapitsa's speech was broadcast abroad, although no reference to such a broadcast can be found. Earlier, on July 6, 1941, Kapitsa had directed a broadcast particularly to British men of science and, although he did not appear to mention atomic matters, he appealed for close cooperation.

also have been caused by a sudden imposition of censorship following official recognition, for the first time, that nuclear energy had military implications.

Beyond this unsupported speculation, we know nothing about whether or how the Soviet administrative authorities reacted to Kapitsa's remark. In any event, by the time it was made, it was too late for the Russians to do anything about atomic bombs until the military crisis had passed. Kapitsa may have said too much too late.

This incident casts further light on the relationship between science and government in the Soviet Union. If Kapitsa was speaking frankly—and there is no reason to suppose the contrary—his work, and presumably that of all the scientists under his direction at the Institute of Physical Problems, was previously exclusively "pure." Somehow the government's preference for applied research had been evaded, or had not been enforced. Conversely, the impact of the German attack may have led to a change of mind among some scientists, at least over the question of pure *versus* applied research. Kapitsa's speech itself indicated a willingness to devote scientific knowledge to the immediate needs at the front. Five months later he was more explicit:

In peacetime it may occasionally have been possible to censure our scientists for not being invariably able to direct their work into channels most useful for the practical needs of our national economy. It may have been possible to reproach them for that academic abstraction, a hangover of the past, which sometimes marked the scientific work of some researchers. But now the threat to their freedom and their desire to save their country has inspired our scientists and directed their efforts toward the solution of present-day tasks. They are all striving urgently to supply answers to the questions put to them by the war.[3]

It may be, then, that the issue of pure *versus* applied research becomes genuinely contradictory only in periods of crisis. If so, the conflict over this issue between the scientists and the new Soviet regime in the twenties and thirties could have arisen because the scientists may have refused to recognize that Russia was facing a crisis. They may have felt that the Russian economy, impoverished and dislocated by World War I, could be set on its feet by normal methods. But the Bolshevik leaders felt compelled not only to rehabilitate the economy but also to transform it into something radically new. The Bolsheviks, in other words, believed that Russia was facing a real crisis; hence, possibly, the conflict over the issue of the true role of science. In World War II, however, scientists and government could agree that Russia was facing a crisis, and the relationship between pure and applied science could cease to be an issue.

Even if the Russians in 1939–41 had thoroughly examined the question of direct military use of atomic energy, they probably would have evaluated the potential new source of energy differently from the British and Americans. For one thing, the explosive properties of fission would probably not have excited the Russians as much as they did the Americans because strategic bombing was not at that time a primary mode of warfare in Soviet military thinking. The Russians, therefore, would have been unlikely to authorize the industrial readjustment and the tremendous expenditures necessary for developing an atom bomb. They probably would have been so impressed by the extremely high cost and rarity of fissionable material that they would have had to rule it out as a replacement for high explosives. Perhaps also the Russians believed that the weapon itself would be too heavy and bulky to be carried by any aircraft available to them or planned for a foreseeable future. Just that question, in fact, was raised by Einstein in his 1939 letter to President Roosevelt, when he suggested that "such bombs might very well prove to be too heavy for transportation by air." (German scientists also were thinking of the atomic weapon as something the size of a monstrous pile of uranium and graphite.) Accordingly, even if the Soviet politicians did give any thought at all to the subject of atomic energy during the 1939–41 period, they would have been quite likely, along with the scientists, to focus their interest primarily or even exclusively on its industrial potential.

This interest is certainly visible in many of the nontechnical articles about atomic energy that were published during the years under discussion. The tone of optimism in some of these articles suggests a genuine interest in atoms for industry. The political events of that period may have colored Soviet views on this matter, for the dawn of the atomic era happened to coincide with what might have seemed to the Russians the eve of a period of easy victories for communism. For the first time since the Bolsheviks had seized power, Lenin's prophecies about the last stage of capitalism seemed about to be fulfilled. The major powers in the capitalist world were engaged in destroying one another. The Soviet Union might preside over the ruins. The Kremlin conceived of the war that broke out in 1939 as a war of attrition. Before the Soviet Union was forced into the conflict, the Bolsheviks probably believed that when all the belligerents had been worn down they would be ripe for revolution.*

Therefore, in looking forward to the postwar era when the USSR would emerge untouched, the Kremlin would no doubt have looked with favor on any radically new resource that might promise a boost to the still backward Soviet economy. The immediate problem in the years 1939–41 was to

---

* There is concrete proof that the Kremlin believed in 1940 that revolution would actually occur. See Franz Borkenau, *European Communism*, Faber, London, 1953, *passim*. For example (p. 308), the French Communist Party received the "line" from the Soviet Embassy: "The situation is described as revolutionary; the conquest of power by the communists is approaching (but, by implication, not yet imminent)."

build a huge military establishment to deter the "imperialist" powers from directing their armies against the "land of
socialism." For that purpose, atomic energy could not have
seemed to have any significance. But for the promising future
—after Germany, France, and Great Britain lay exhausted
and the proletariat of those countries brought them into the
communist fold—atomic energy might have seemed to promise an additional bonus. Soviet interest in increasing Russia's
economic potential cannot be overemphasized. Lenin's
slogan of 1920, "Communism is Soviet power plus the electrification of the entire country," has been one of those most
frequently reiterated during the last forty years.

Moreover, economic strength has always been valued
highly by Soviet leaders as a basic factor in military might.
Consequently, concentrating on the industrial use of atomic
energy probably did not, in their view, diminish its potential
contribution to their military power. Soviet interest in the
industrial atom in 1941 may, in fact, have persisted longer
than military foresight should have permitted; for, even
when the Soviet Union resumed its nuclear program in 1943,
Soviet scientists continued to emphasize, in public statements, its industrial application. The same attitude may
have adversely affected Soviet calculations about atomic
energy even after Hiroshima, and thus may have contributed
to the lag in Soviet thinking about atomic warfare. For there
is much evidence that the Russians placed low value on the
military significance of atomic weapons for several years after
the war, perhaps simply because of the blunt fact that they
had no atomic weapon and were really not quite sure whether
they could ever successfully develop one.

In any event, whether or not the primary interest in industrial uses of atomic energy expressed in Soviet public
statements in the 1939–41 period was based on fact, the

political advantages in taking this line were great. Until
Russia was brought into the war, Soviet propagandists
claimed that most of the capitalist world was engaged in
destruction while the communist system was "demonstrably"
concentrating on peaceful labor (they did not, of course,
refer to the military importance of a strong industrial base).
A peaceful Soviet atom could not but enhance that picture.

5

THE DORMANT PERIOD

Although the prewar atomic research programs in the Soviet Union and in the West were quite similar, the official attitudes in the East and West toward the significance of the research findings were apparently quite different. One basic difference seems to be reflected in the Soviet decision to halt its atomic research program after the German invasion of Russia. Russians who referred to this decision at the time seemed to feel that atomic research could not lead to anything useful for World War II; they revealed no trace of anxiety at having given up something of immediate value.

The word "decision" in this connection may not be entirely appropriate. The serious damage caused by the first German assault would no doubt have forced the Russians to stop work in nuclear physics even if they had wanted to continue. The pressure of war and the confusion resulting from it may have prevented Soviet political leaders from even thinking about the fate of nuclear research.

The scientists did think about it, however. Kapitsa alluded, in 1943, to the factors that had influenced scientific decisions two years before. He said that the exigencies of war had made it necessary to concentrate almost exclusively on oxygen:

Directing all its workers to these tasks, the Institute [of Physical Problems] was forced to reduce considerably its work in the fields I mentioned at the beginning of my address [namely, low temperatures, the atomic nucleus, and the solid body—which Kapitsa had listed as the most promising fields of physics] . . . . *Our point was that scientific work which is not completed and produces no results during the war may even be harmful if it diverts our forces from work which is more urgently required* [italics supplied].[1]

Doubtless, too, the severe stress on Soviet industry also made it impossible to think of trying to develop an atomic bomb during World War II. This Soviet problem was analogous to a similar one that faced Germany. Werner Heisenberg, a prominent figure in the German atomic energy project, described the situation in Germany as follows:

. . . the [atomic energy] project could not have succeeded under German war conditions. It could not have succeeded on technical grounds alone; for even in America, with its much greater resources in scientific men, technicians and industrial potential, and with an economy undisturbed by enemy action, the bomb was not ready until after the conclusion of the war with Germany. In particular, a German atomic bomb project would not have succeeded because of the military situation. In 1942, German industry was already stretched to the limit,* the German Army had suffered serious reverses in Russia in the winter of 1941–1942, and enemy air superiority was beginning to make itself felt. The immediate production of armaments could be robbed neither

* This was not actually the case as early as 1942. But Heisenberg's testimony indicates that German scientific experts *believed* it to be true, and their attitude would certainly have led to the kind of advice that Heisenberg attributed to them.

of personnel nor of raw materials, nor could the enormous plants required have been effectively protected against air attack. Finally—and this is a most important fact—the undertaking could not be initiated against the psychological background of the men responsible for German war policy. These men expected an early decision of the war, even in 1942, and any major project which did not promise quick returns was specifically forbidden. To obtain the necessary support, the experts would have been obliged to promise early results, knowing that these promises could not be kept. Faced with this situation, the experts did not attempt to advocate with the supreme command a great industrial effort for the production of atomic bombs.[2]

The Soviet scientists were as disinclined to make unrealistic promises to Stalin as the German scientists were to Hitler, especially since there were probably some among them who doubted that militarily effective atomic energy could be obtained in time to be of any use in World War II. No doubt there were similar differences of opinion among German scientists, as there were also in America. Yet, unlike American scientists, neither Russian nor German specialists seem to have urged their governments to take the full risk. In addition, of course, the Soviet Union may have had some intelligence on the state of atomic development in Germany; this would have reassured them about the impossibility that their principal enemy might develop atomic weapons in time to affect the outcome of the war. There is no evidence of anxiety about the likelihood of German achievement of atomic weapons.

Concrete evidence of Soviet atomic espionage in Germany appears to be unavailable, though the search has not been exhaustive. It is considered likely, however, that the Russians had some information about atomic research in all countries where it was being conducted. If so, the Russians probably knew in 1941–45 what we learned only late in the war: that the German atomic effort was so meager we had nothing to fear. Professor Samuel A. Goudsmit, who led the U.S. investigation of the German nuclear effort, reported that "the whole German uranium setup was on a ludicrously small scale,"[3] and that German security measures concealing their work in atomic energy were "not of a very high standard." For example, German draft deferment requests contained the clear and unclassified justification "Working on Energy Production from Uranium."[4]

While there is no direct evidence, it is highly probable that the Soviet Union was conducting espionage operations on the German atomic energy program. The most likely channel for this information would have been through the activities of the "Rote Kapelle" (Red Orchestra), the code name for a major Red espionage organization in Germany.[5, 6] The German leader of the Rote Kapelle was Lieutenant Colonel Schultze-Boysen. He held an important post in Goering's Air Ministry, which in the last half of 1942 took over the German atomic energy project. But more important is the fact that the Rote Kapelle reported to the same "Director" in Moscow as the Canadian spy ring reported to. The "Director" was fully aware of the requirements on atomic energy information and could have directed the Rote Kapelle to gather data on that subject if he so desired.

The single Soviet mention of German atomic weapons work found by the author appeared in 1943 and may have been motivated by wholly political considerations rather than by genuine fear. It appeared in a booklet entitled *The Latest Discoveries of Modern Atomic Physics in the Light of Dialectical Materialism* by Professor Ernst Yaromirovich Kolman. In this instance Kolman referred to German work on an atomic bomb (citing the American and Swiss press as authorities) as proof of the manner in which "German fascists" perverted science for aggressive purposes. (For over a quarter of a century Kolman has been one of the Soviet Union's outstanding interpreters of the role of ideology in physics, but he probably had minute, if any, access to official sources of information.)

By contrast, fear of possible German progress in nuclear work was one of the important factors that spurred on American scientists and engineers in the Manhattan Project. The war memoirs of Western political and military leaders reproduce numerous messages from the Kremlin reporting evidence of various German technical developments that were viewed as threatening the Soviet Union. But none of these messages includes even a single mention of the German atomic energy program. If the Russians had feared German success in atomic development, they would almost certainly have urged the United States to accelerate its own effort, as they did several times with respect to other weapons. The fact that they did not do this cannot be attributed to an information security policy because atomic energy was being openly mentioned in Soviet publications during this period. The Russians, who held German technical skill and industrial might in high esteem, may have believed, further, that if the Germans did not expect a quick payoff, it was unrealistic for the Soviet Union to expect one from its own atomic energy program.

Nor is it likely that available information about other foreign efforts in this field led the Soviet Union to a different conclusion. Even if, at the time, the United States, unlike Germany, had appeared capable of producing an atomic weapon in time to affect the course of the war, the Russians might still have curtailed their own program. For after June 1941 the United States and the United Kingdom were allied with the USSR, and although the Russians must have considered the relationship to be temporary and expedient, nevertheless the possibility that the Anglo-Americans might develop atomic weapons would have held no *immediate* threat for the Soviet Union.

The possibility did not seem great in any case. Atomic developments in the United States, at least until the end of 1941, would probably not have alarmed the Russians even if they had known about the optimistic conclusions of the Thomson and Jewett committees. What is more, with full knowledge of the American program and of the opinions of the scientists engaged in it, they would probably have arrived at conclusions similar to those concerning the German program. For, as Dr. Smyth later reported, by the end of 1941,

No chain reaction had been achieved; no appreciable amount of U-235 had been separated from U-238; only minute amounts of Pu-239 had been produced; the production of large quantities of uranium metal, heavy water, beryllium, and pure graphite was still largely in the discussion stage.[7]

Though Smyth also cites progress that offset these limitations, the over-all results of two years of concentrated attention and effort by the foremost American physicists probably would not have impressed the Russians. Moreover, there were still prominent nuclear physicists in the United States who were skeptical about the feasibility of achieving an atomic weapon.

Just how much the Soviets learned of the U.S. and British wartime nuclear program through espionage is, to say the least, controversial. Perhaps a more pertinent question would concern the extent to which the intelligence was appreciated at the time of its collection. In all probability, the collected information was not put to its best use until four or five years later.

The available evidence about Soviet atomic espionage indicates that the earliest activity in the field dates from 1942, when Klaus Fuchs began volunteering information to the Soviet authorities. There is no evidence that the Soviet espionage network was concerned with securing information on foreign nuclear developments at the time, in 1940, when the subject became shrouded in secrecy in the West. Yet, even after the Russians had begun to gather intelligence on Western atomic programs, they did not give first priority to the collection of atomic secrets. This indicates that, even after 1942, the indifference to atomic science that we have noted continued to color the official attitude. This, if true, strengthens the hypothesis that, despite the impressive early advances of Soviet nuclear science, the Soviet government did not see, or did not take seriously, the military implications of the atom until, probably, well after the war.

Curiosity of Soviet spies about any given subject is not *ipso facto* a reflection of unusually active interest in that subject on the part of the Politburo. In the Soviet system, espionage is a reflex action. It seems to react to outside stimuli without regard to the policy of the Kremlin. Also, at least until Beria's removal in 1953, the Ministry of State Security (MGB)* was nearly an autonomous administrative organ within the Soviet state and determined its range of activities independently. It could have taken an interest in collecting data on atomic energy without a knowledge of other organs of the government, or, for that matter, of most of the members of the Politburo.† Such MGB action would have been possible even if other governmental organs—including Politburo members—had no interest in the subject.

---

* The relationships of the Ministry of Internal Affairs (MVD) to the MGB, their historical genesis from the OGPU, NKVD, etc., to the present KGB, and the various personalities like Beria from period to period are so complex that an extensive treatise would be required to define them. It suffices this particular study to treat the organizations as a single entity, although there is actually a well-defined partition of their responsibilities.

† An example of the pack-rat nature of Soviet espionage techniques is given by the case of Rista Ilić, an assistant reader at the Faculty of Engineering in Belgrade, Yugoslavia, who in 1949 was required by the Soviets to submit "everything he had heard or read about the applica-

The MGB itself, so far as the available evidence shows, placed no priority on efforts to secure atomic data. The conviction and trial in the West of several Soviet agents who had gathered atomic data may prove only that U.S. and British officials guarded atomic secrets more vigilantly than they did other military secrets. It does not prove unusual interest on the part of the Russians. In fact, there is concrete evidence that the Soviet *military* espionage ring in Canada seemed to attach no priority to atomic energy as late as the spring and summer of 1945. The *Report of the Royal Commission* on this case cites seventeen tasks assigned to Zabotin, Motinov, and Rogov during the period from March to August 1945—a list, the Commission observes, that should not be considered exhaustive. Only two of these requirements dealt with atomic energy.

If the Kremlin had been vitally interested in atomic energy, one would expect to find that there was a central coordinating office sifting and studying the incoming data. There is nothing in the published data about Soviet espionage to indicate that such an office existed. Furthermore, there is some evidence that agents may not have been receiving efficient direction from Moscow; at least this seems to have been true with respect to the Canadian spy ring. As late as August 31, 1945, the chief military espionage agent begged his superior in Moscow to give him better guidance.

A third foreign program that the Russians could have

---

tion of atomic energy in military science." It is surprising that the Soviet intermediaries would not recognize beforehand that the value of his possible contribution would be nil. The few items that he did submit were trivial, to say the most for them. It is more plausible to think that the atomic energy assignments were given Ilić to give him a sense of importance and that the Yugoslav economic and political information that he also passed was of much greater interest to the Soviets. This elliptical technique of exciting the enthusiasm of the collector may have been operative in other instances of Soviet recruitment.

used for guidance in making their estimate of the military importance of atomic energy was that of Japan. Japan had able nuclear physicists, respectable instruments for research and experimentation, and a clear understanding of the theoretical possibilities of producing an atomic bomb. But the Japanese scientists who were working on the project itself were not optimistic about achieving a weapon in time to be useful in World War II. They were overwhelmed by the technical difficulties involved in separating U-235, and presumably also by the expense it would involve. Like the German physicists, they did not dare to advise their government that an atomic weapon could be manufactured. In fact, one of them is reported to have predicted that the United States would find the technical difficulties insuperable. Consequently, the Japanese program was never given adequate financial or administrative support.

If the Russians knew* how meager the Japanese program was, despite the fact that it had a basis for serious expansion, and if they knew how pessimistic the Japanese scientists were, they would have felt that Japanese as well as German experience confirmed their opinion that there was no basis for fearing atomic weapons from the enemy. Moreover, Japan was not then an immediate enemy.

So small was the Soviet interest in, or fear of, the military potentialities of atomic energy in the early war years that no censorship restrictions were placed on the subject even

---

* It would seem likely that Sorge, the Soviet espionage agent in Japan, would have picked up data about the Japanese atomic program. But even if he did not, the Soviet Embassy in Tokyo would probably have at least sensed that no large-scale atomic program was under way. Yamashita ("Japan's Uncompleted Atomic Bomb," *Kaizo*, Special Number, November 15, 1952, pp. 162–65) observed that the three secret weapons programs into which the army put its greatest efforts became rather widely known despite stringent security measures; he used that fact as a basis for demonstrating that there was no major effort devoted to atomic energy: if there had been, he argued, information about it would have leaked to the public.

after the German attack had forced a sharp curtailment of the Soviet program.

Failure to conceal their weakness in nuclear research after 1941 would seem to be further proof either that Soviet leaders were still unaware of the military implications of atomic energy, or that they had concluded that the Germans did not take seriously the military possibilities of atomic energy. For the Russians would probably have imposed a censorship on references to the subject, at least as a bluff, if they had thought the Germans were sufficiently concerned about it generally to worry about the possibility that Russia might develop an atomic weapon. Some public references to the American program made by the Russians after the Soviet-American alliance indicated that they were so unconcerned about atomic energy that they were careless about helping maintain the curtain of silence the Western allies had drawn over the subject in the spring of 1940. For example, the Soviet censor would certainly have blue-penciled *Pravda*'s report of Kapitsa's remark about the theoretical yield of an atomic bomb if Soviet authorities had been anxious about a real potential in atomic energy. The fact that he didn't indicates that Russian indifference was considerable. They apparently assumed the Germans were so little concerned with the subject that there was no point in Russia's even trying to assist the United States in a bluff of the kind mentioned above.

Again, if the Russians had given atomic energy much serious attention, they would probably have exploited American and British concern over it to the Soviet Union's political advantage. If they had known that the Americans and British were to some degree hopeful of success in releasing atomic energy on a large scale, possibly even for use in weapons, the Russians, predisposed to waging political warfare, would have kept the Western Allies in the dark about Soviet potentialities for developing nuclear weapons. In other words, Russia's position in the alliance with the West would have been strengthened had Russia concealed the fact that the once-strong Soviet atomic program had been virtually abandoned in June 1941.* Instead, the Russians openly published data revealing that it had been abandoned. These data were freely exported to foreign nations, although they were not widely read at that time.

It seems obvious, therefore, that the Russians exercised no censorship in this field during the prewar and early war years. Until June 1941, the Soviet scientific literature apparently described the entire atomic program then in progress; and after June 1941, it revealed that this program had been curtailed to the point of extinction.

In fact, the Russians went beyond merely allowing publication of the results of nuclear research. They apparently went out of their way to publicize their progress. Articles on nuclear research appeared in the principal newspapers and in popular-science magazines with wide circulation. Moreover, most of these articles were published after both the Western Allies and Germany had dropped a curtain of silence over the subject of atomic energy.

As early as the spring of 1939, an informal group of foreign-born U.S. physicists, cognizant of the possible military application of atomic energy, had enlisted the aid of Niels Bohr in trying to stop the publication of fission data by voluntary agreement. However, Joliot-Curie refused to cooperate, and publication in the West continued freely for about another year. In April 1940, two months before the fall of France, a formal U.S. censorship committee was formed, and thenceforth publication on the subject of nu-

---

* Presumably the Russians would have assumed that the United States and Britain *knew* how far advanced in nuclear research the USSR had been in 1941, since their scientific publications had revealed it.

clear fission virtually ceased in the journals of the free world; the first major breach of silence was the release of the *Smyth Report* in August 1945. By the spring of 1940, German scientific literature also had begun to omit references to atomic work, although some items did slip through.

But throughout 1940 and well into 1941, by contrast, the Soviet press, both technical and popular, gave more publicity to atomic energy than ever before. On March 28, 1940, *Izvestiia* reported a public lecture by Ioffe, in which he gave the atomic nucleus first priority among three problems in physics that he considered to be of primary interest to the Soviet Union. In this lecture, Ioffe cited Kurchatov as the principal figure working on this problem and also described some of the details of the design of the cyclotron then under construction at the Leningrad Physico-Technical Institute.

In May 1940, there was an article in a popular-science magazine entitled "Some Problems of the Physics of the Atomic Nucleus." In June, the new Leningrad cyclotron was again described to the public in *Izvestiia*. On November 23, Ioffe delivered a popular lecture at the Polytechnical Museum at Moscow, in which he gave an elementary explanation of the process of spontaneous fission and praised the young scientists Flerov and Petrzhak for their original discoveries in this field.

Enthusiasm over the achievements of 1940 was publicly exhibited on New Year's Eve. Soviet newspapers often use this occasion to review the past and speculate about the future. *Izvestiia* published an article entitled "Uranium 235" that prophesied:

Soviet physical science, young though it is, has marked up great successes in recent years. Next year it will study one of the most fundamental problems: uranium. Extremely interesting research has already been done in this field. . . .
Physics stands at the threshold of discoveries of boundless

significance. We are confronted not only with the fact that mankind will acquire a new source of energy surpassing by a million times everything that has been hitherto known. Nor is our perspective merely that we shall have a "fuel" which will substitute for our depleting supplies of coal and oil and thus rescue industry from a fuel famine. The central fact is that human might is entering a new era. . . .

Man will be able to acquire any quantity of energy he pleases and apply it to any ends he chooses.

In March 1941, a popular-science magazine for youth published an article on "The Problems of Uranium" that told how, late one night in February 1940, after working in the depths of the Moscow subway, Flerov and Petrzhak telephoned Kurchatov (portrayed as a venerable and fatherly professor, though he was actually 37 years of age!) and exclaimed: "Igor Vasilevich, we have just observed the spontaneous fission of uranium!" This is, apparently, a true story. They had set up their instruments in the subway in order to avoid the possibility of stray cosmic rays interfering with the accuracy of their measurements.

A few weeks later, in May 1941, another article appeared in a popular-science magazine, entitled "The Principal Paths of Contemporary Physics." It was written by a distinguished physicist, S. I. Vavilov, who was to become head of the Academy of Sciences in 1945. He wrote:

At the present time research on the atomic nucleus occupies the center of attention of Soviet physics, and especially large resources will be concentrated on this field. Laboratories for nuclear physics exist in the Physico-Technical and Radium Institutes in Leningrad, in the Physical Institute in Moscow and in the Physical Institute in Kharkov. Many dozens of young physicists are working in these laboratories. The laboratories have excellent equipment, and Soviet nuclear physics can produce a number of outstanding results in its field.

Even after the Soviet nuclear program had been dormant for nearly a year and a half, Ioffe reminded the world audience of Soviet interest in the atom and of Soviet participation in studying its secrets. Speaking before a ceremonial session of the Academy of Sciences as late as November 1942, he said: "Soviet physicists have taken a most active part in the most engrossing problems of the last decade—the problems of the atomic nucleus and cosmic rays."[8]

This policy of apparently complete candor about Soviet achievements in the field of nuclear research seemed almost deliberately derisive of the security regulations of Germany and the Western Allies. Both the Soviet government and Soviet scientists, then, were completely candid about Soviet progress in nuclear research. The reasons why each was so, though, may have varied. The scientists may have been interested in publicity as a way of provoking disclosure of information on atomic research by the West. They must have been disappointed when the scientific journals of Germany, Great Britain, and the United States stopped publishing the results of research in the field. They would unquestionably have liked to continue sharing in the findings of foreign physicists; they had profited considerably from such exchanges of information in earlier years.

The Soviet political authorities would no doubt have been willing to cooperate with the scientists in this connection, if the reasons were indeed those suggested above and if the political leaders were aware of the reasons. So far as the government was concerned (and there were probably many patriotic scientists who would have shared this viewpoint), Russia could afford to act irresponsibly regarding the security measures of the belligerent powers. Any atomic data revealed by either side in response to the challenge of Soviet publicity could not but be advantageous to the Russians.

Any consequent harm to either side would have been of no concern to the Russians; in fact it would have pleased them.

In addition, however, the political authorities might have had their own reasons for giving free reign to publicity about their nuclear research program. Knowing, perhaps, of the fears of both belligerents that the other side might produce atomic bombs, and knowing that both had imposed secrecy on the subject, Soviet leaders and scientists alike may have wished to show *both* camps—at least until they themselves entered the war in June 1941—that the Soviet Union was well advanced in the field that interested Germany and the United States and Great Britain so much. If the Russians were so motivated, the Soviet action, then, was a taunt to both sides and a demonstration of the Soviet Union's detachment from both. Psychologically it may have been a kind of bravado. Russians have always felt inferior to the West, and most particularly to Germany and the United States, in the field of technology. In atomic energy, German and American scientists were silenced, and the Russians had a clear field for a limited time to boast about their achievements.

But the hiatus in their nuclear program soon put the Soviets in an obviously inferior nuclear position and from the time of serious resumption of the program in 1943 until the Moscow and Geneva Conferences of 1955, public references to technical progress became very sparse indeed.

6

KEEPING INFORMED

Forced by the immediate pressures of war, the Soviets essentially dropped their atomic energy program in the summer of 1941—at a time when the Western atomic effort was just about to start its phenomenal growth. Less than two years later, just after Western scientists had demonstrated that a nuclear chain reaction was possible, Soviet leaders decided to invest a part of the small reserve of scientific manpower in at least watching and evaluating Western atomic progress.

The technical data on the Soviet wartime atomic energy program suggest that for one or more of several possible reasons, the Soviets were unable or did not choose, even in the latter stages of the war, to initiate an atomic program on so grand a scale as was being unfolded in the United States. The possible reasons for this low priority of effort are:

1. The physical and manpower resources, except for the bare minimum necessary to keep the USSR technically in-

formed of U.S. progress, were simply not available for what must have been considered a task unnecessary to the successful ending of the war.

2. The full import of the size and seriousness of the Western atomic program may not have been impressed upon the minds of Soviet leaders busy with the immediate problems of war. This may have been due in part to the lack of coordinated reporting by the various Soviet intelligence services.

3. The Soviet political and/or scientific leaders may have been skeptical about the possibility of making an atomic bomb.

4. The military value of the atomic bomb may have been underestimated.

Victor Kravchenko, a former staff member of the Soviet State Defense Committee, reported that toward the end of 1942 Stalin held a meeting with the head of the Academy of Sciences, Professor Komarov, and with Academician Kapitsa on the subject of atomic energy. Whether or not the report has substance, this period does seem to mark the beginning of renewed interest in atomic energy on the part of the Soviets. More significantly, Kravchenko reported that Soviet military intelligence was at that time exerting itself to obtain atomic secrets from other countries.[1]

It is evident from the information made public at the espionage trials of Allan Nunn May, Klaus Fuchs, and others, that the Soviets were all too well informed during the war on the progress of the joint U.S., British, and Canadian atomic effort.

The role that Donald MacLean might have played in providing the USSR with information on joint U.S. and British atomic policy matters is suspect. As First Secretary of the British Embassy at Washington from 1944 to 1948, Mac-Lean was a member of the highly secret Combined Policy

Committee, which controlled the distribution of atomic raw materials and, of necessity, had access to stockpile figures for those ores. Information on the situation that prevailed in the early postwar years—when the supply of uranium, without which there could not be an atomic energy industry, was sparse—could have given valuable guidance to the Soviets during the formation of their postwar atomic policy. The U.S. "tightening" of atomic information exchange with its wartime working Allies, Great Britain and Canada, was a subject of long and heated debate in the Combined Policy Committee. The insight relating to the possible postwar atomic strength and policy of the United States, as available to a member of the Combined Policy Committee, would constitute significant background material for the formative stages of Soviet atomic policy. Although MacLean did not defect to the Soviets until May 1951, the British White Paper[2] cites strong evidence to support the assertion that he was a Soviet agent long before that. MacLean undoubtedly was one of a multitude of Soviet agents seeking, almost helter-skelter, information on all phases of U.S. technical, military, and economic programs.

The eager (and sometimes naïve) enthusiasm for any information about the U.S. Manhattan Project is illustrated by the experience of William L. White upon a visit to the Electrosila plant at Leningrad in the summer of 1944. He described the persistent questioning of his guide, Kirilov:

But Kirilov doggedly went on. "Behind Urals we have many big things. We have like you call in America, Manhattan Project. You know this, yes?"

"Oh, of course," I said. "We have lots of war projects in New York."

"Not in New York," said Kirilov, looking at me intently, "Manhattan Project. You know of this?"

"But Manhattan," I said, "is a part of New York. Of course, I know Manhattan. I live there."

It was not until an entire year had passed—and the atomic bomb went off at Hiroshima—that I understood, at last, exactly what it was that poor, stammering Kirilov had been trying to ask me.[8]

Despite the unsuccessful efforts of agents like Kirilov, the information gathered from other sources was extensive. There were also a few "security leaks" that may have come to the attention of Soviet agents outside the program. In 1945, Alexander Sachs quoted a serious leak in the *Minerals Yearbook* for 1943. Actually, the 1943 *Yearbook* was not printed until 1945, so the data were at least two years old when disclosed. Major General L. R. Groves, wartime leader of the Manhattan Project, described "a very serious break" on the mechanism for making the atomic bomb. "If I had been a Russian," he stated, "I think of the intelligence of Kapitsa and the background or the intelligence of anyone else who was working on this project—it [the article] would have indicated that the way to produce an atomic bomb was in some way to take care that it might be based on implosion." The article to which General Groves referred was in the November 27, 1944, issue of *Time*. But a review of these and other "leaks" indicates that they were of minor importance compared with the information transmitted to the Soviet Union by "atomic spies."

Very little is known about the manner in which intelligence data are processed in the USSR. It is known, from the Canadian spy trial and other sources, that there were parellel networks serving the Soviet Union. Much of the information obtained by agents of one network was unknown to the agents of another. There is even some evidence that at a high level at Moscow the data on atomic developments obtained by espionage were not coordinated.

It is therefore possible that information gathered abroad may have remained compartmentalized within the Soviet

Union. Indeed, it appears to be possible that the full import of atomic developments in the United States did not become clear to Soviet leaders (because of defective operation of the Soviet intelligence-evaluation system) until the first bomb was tested. The necessary result would have been a failure on the part of responsible Soviet authorities to set in motion a Soviet atomic energy program because of ignorance. But the same result could have occurred even with a perfectly functioning system.

Assume, for the sake of this argument, that both the collection and evaluation processes were perfect. This would mean first that the Russians had available to them all the details not only about the American but also about the German atomic energy program. Further, there would have been a group of Soviet nuclear physicists to whom all this information would have been given for evaluation and who, in turn, would be fully informed about all aspects of the Soviet Union's own research program. Finally, there would have been a smoothly functioning channel by which the findings of the scientists would have been converted into meaningful recommendations on the basis of which the Politburo (or at that time, the State Defense Committee) would make policy decisions regarding a Soviet atomic energy program. It is probable that the latter channel would be in the person of a close adviser to Stalin (perhaps Malenkov).

Malenkov's wartime positions make it likely that he would have played this role. Moreover, Malenkov may have had special knowledge of Soviet atomic espionage during the war by virtue of his position as head of the Foreign Section of the Central Committee of the Communist Party of the Soviet Union in Moscow, which he held at least in 1942 and presumably later. There is a clear implication in the Canadian report that Goussarov, Second Secretary of the Soviet Embassy in Ottawa, reported directly to Malenkov; if, as is probable, Goussarov was gathering atomic data, the supposition is that Malenkov was aware of atomic matters from at least that network. But such a weighty decision as the commitment of resources to the development of atomic bombs would have been made only by Stalin himself.

Given this system, it is possible to speculate on what kind of decision, if any, would be the end result. The nuclear physicist would likely have advised Malenkov during the 1942–45 period of the following:

1. The major effort put into an atomic energy research and development program by the United States was beginning to promise very interesting results—particularly after the chain reaction was achieved at the University of Chicago in 1942.

2. It would be most desirable from the Soviet point of view to ensure continued surveillance of the U.S. program and, if possible, to intensify the espionage effort.

3. Despite the remarkable progress made by the Manhattan Project, it was impossible to predict *when* fissionable materials could be packaged in a practicable weapon; it might be several years.

4. The process required for the extraction of U-235 from uranium ore would be extremely difficult, and the industrial resources needed for producing U-235 in quantities significant for military purposes would be colossal.

5. The world supply of uranium ore might be insufficient to provide enough fissionable material to permit the production of a militarily important number of atomic weapons.

6. The power of such weapons, if developed, would be so great that their only efficient military use would be in strategic bombing.

Provided with such advice from Soviet scientists, Stalin's right-hand man would consider the implications in the con-

text of the totality of problems facing the Kremlin. Of
overwhelming importance was the German invasion of
Russia. Until the spring of 1943, the Russians were fighting
a strategically defensive war. The expenditure of resources
for that purpose was enormous, and it had to be supported by
an industrial system seriously depleted under German attack
and occupation and by lend-lease supplies that reached the
Soviet Union over long and vulnerable supply routes.

Though the spring of 1943 was, in retrospect, the unmis-
takable turning point of the war on the eastern front, Stalin
was apparently not entirely reassured by the victory of Stalingrad and the rollback of the German armies along the entire
front. He was suspicious of the American-British delay in
opening a western front; and, in February and March, he
displayed probably genuine (if nevertheless paranoid) fear
that the postponement of operations in North Africa was
deliberate, claiming on March 15 that the dilatory actions of
his Western Allies had made it possible for the Germans to
transfer 36 divisions from the west to the Russian theater.
These were only high points in a series of expressions of sus-
picion and anger directed against the West after the most
critical phases of the war in Russia had passed. Many of the
suspicions, such as the charge made in the autumn of 1942
that influential people in Britain were seeking a separate
peace, meant that the Kremlin was uneasy lest the entire
capitalist world turn its forces against the USSR. In these
circumstances, the Soviet leadership could not feel that certain victory was in sight; thus the luxury of developing a
new but remote explosive force could not be permitted.

Even if the Soviets had been sure that victory over Germany was the only problem they had to worry about, there
was still a large effort required to achieve it. Their industrial
potential had been seriously diminished by military destruction. It is inconceivable that a responsible political adviser

would have recommended to Stalin, at least before the turning point at Stalingrad, that any industrial resources whatsoever be diverted for the development of atomic energy.

In the light of advice from scientists, then, weighed with the political and military situation, Stalin's adviser would have had three choices regarding his briefing of Stalin:

1. Advise him to go all out in the development and production of fissionable materials and weapons.
2. Recommend against any program of development at least until after the war.
3. Refrain from mentioning the subject of atomic energy at all.

The adviser would certainly have rejected the first choice in the light of the expert advice that we have postulated above. The second and third choices seem to be about equally reasonable for him to have made. Actually the second is the more reasonable of the two because it would have been in keeping with his dual responsibility: (1) to keep Stalin informed of developments that might later become important; and (2) to give his chief the best advice possible, based on information obtained from experts and evaluated in the light of current problems facing the Soviet Union. It is, of course, possible that Malenkov (if it were indeed he) took the third choice on the grounds that the information from abroad did not indicate a serious enough problem to warrant bothering the boss: Stalin should not be distracted from other concerns by relatively trivial events. The adviser might also have chosen to keep Stalin in ignorance of a new and fundamental scientific discovery abroad out of fear that Stalin might be stimulated, by jealousy and feelings of inferiority toward the West, to order immediate emulation of the U.S. effort in atomic energy and thus divert to this program industrial resources that were vitally needed for the current conduct of war. It is also possible that Stalin's adviser would be afraid to admit to him that Soviet science lagged behind the West in this field.

If Stalin had not been briefed at all during the war about American atomic developments, this would explain his apparent ignorance or indifference when President Truman announced to him at Potsdam in July 1945 that a new weapon had just been tested and would be used against Japan. Stalin's reception of this news might also be consistent with his having been informed months before about the American program, but having been advised that it was relatively insignificant. In this event, Stalin might actually have forgotten the earlier intelligence when Truman spoke to him on July 24, or perhaps he felt that the President was exaggerating the power of the new weapon.

Regardless of whether or not Stalin was informed prior to Truman's announcement, the policy of the Soviet leadership regarding atomic energy during the war period can be inferred. First, obviously a decision was made to defer a large-scale development program for the time being. Second, Soviet espionage networks were instructed to gather data on the American program. Third, on a modest scale, Soviet nuclear physicists must have been ordered or permitted to continue their research work. This policy involved the minimum diversion of resources, yet laid a foundation for a concentrated effort when the exigencies of war would no longer prevent it.

There were certain impediments that kept the USSR from launching an atomic program during the war, but there were also advantages to be gained by deferring such a program. There was the very real uncertainty about whether an atomic bomb was feasible. Even the scientists on the Manhattan Project could not be sure, until July 1945, that it would work. Therefore, it was advantageous to the Rus-

sians, who possessed a good espionage network, to profit by
U.S. experimentation. If the United States should fail, they
could avoid the bypaths along which the Americans had
erred, and there would be no problem of U.S. superiority in
this field after the war. If the United States should succeed—
they could have calculated in 1943 through July 1945—they
would be able to begin their program on the basis of U.S.
findings and would be assured of the results. Moreover, after
the victory at Stalingrad they could look forward to the complete defeat and possible occupation of Germany, knowing,
as they must have, that Germany was also working on atomic
energy. The Russians could expect to seize both German
scientists and technicians and perhaps atomic installations.
This they finally did, to some extent.

During the war, the Russians had no reason to be greatly
concerned about the lead in an atomic energy program that
the United States would have over them by the end of the
war. Well informed as they were of U.S. progress they would
have known through espionage data that the American stockpile of atomic bombs—if the United States actually succeeded
in mastering the technique of manufacturing a weapon at
all—would be insignificant for military purposes for a long
time after the first weapon was produced. Therefore, they
would have time, since they could begin their program from
the top of the plateau already reached, to plan and put into
operation an atomic energy program that would enable them
to catch up with the United States before the U.S. stockpile
could become a matter of concern militarily. This line of
reasoning had a sound basis in the generally recognized economic and technological phenomenon of the behavior of
industrially backward nations after they enter the industrial
age; at a later stage, their industry advances by leaps and
bounds largely because of the experience borrowed from the
predecessors. Communist doctrine also would have been

reassuring to the Russians on this point. One of the basic Communist theories concerning economic progress postulates that it is only in a socialist society that the "productive relations" (the organization of society particularly with respect to its involvement in producing goods) are in consonance with the "productive forces" (the inanimate means of production). From this "fact" several advantages accrue to the socialist state. One of them is that the rate of industrial development is far greater than is possible under capitalism. Stalin stated in 1931 that "our system, the Soviet system, endows us with potentialities for fast industrial advance forward of which not a single bourgeois country can dream."[4]

If the Russians preferred not to rely wholly on their intelligence organs for information on which to base estimates of the progress of the American atomic energy program, they had means to cross check at least the strategic implications that could be perceived in the intelligence data: during the latter part of the war the United States and Britain revealed to the Russians their military plans for terminating the war with Germany and Japan. Through this source of information, the Russians would have learned that as late as February 1945 (at the Yalta Conference) the United States was not including atomic armament in any of its long-range planning for winning the war. And the planning at that time did not foresee an end of the war—at least of the Japanese sector of it—within the short period that was actually in prospect. If the United States had intended then to place any reliance on atomic weapons within the indefinite war time period ahead, the fact would probably have been revealed to the Russians. Since no new weapon was mentioned, the Russians would have concluded (assuming that Stalin and his staff even knew about the U.S. atomic energy program then) that the United States did not expect to possess a usable atomic weapon for an indefinite time. Even if the Russians did not expect candor from the United States (though the spirit of U.S. military reports to the Russians at Yalta apparently would have indicated such a disposition), the planning that was announced would not seem to imply that the United States actually looked forward to anything different from conventional warfare. Though intensive bombing of the Japanese mainland was an important part of the announced program, the elaborate plans to shift troops from Europe to the Far East and, most important, the appeal to the Russians for aid in defeating Japan would almost certainly have meant to the Russians that the United States was not counting on a quick victory through the use of unconventional weapons.

Secretary of State Stettinius, because of reports of Soviet espionage activities on the West Coast, had felt that the Russians themselves might bring up the subject at Yalta. He discussed this possibility with General Marshall and President Roosevelt. The latter "agreed with the General's position that we should handle any Russian questions if and as they arose." The fact that such questions, although fully expected, did not arise does not indicate strong Soviet concern about the atomic bomb at that time.

It is clear that at the time of Yalta, U.S. and British planners felt they could not, with any degree of reliability, take into account an atomic bomb capability. Apparently, a series of technical briefings in September 1944 marked the beginning of a conviction on the part of President Roosevelt and Prime Minister Churchill that the atomic bomb program could soon be brought to an effective conclusion. However, civilian and military aides were not as convinced.

Admiral Leahy stated that he "still did not have much confidence in the practicability of the project."[5] He admitted after the war that he had "misjudged the terrible efficiency of this entirely new concept of explosive."[6] Stettinius recorded the feeling of the military at Yalta: "I knew at Yalta,

for instance, of the immense pressure put on the President
by our military leaders to bring Russia into the Far Eastern
War. At this time the atomic bomb was still an unknown
quantity."⁷ James Byrnes indicated that there was still a
great deal of doubt concerning the atomic bomb effort as late
as April 1. Other sources indicate quite similar uncertain-
ties.

Churchill, although an enthusiastic supporter of the
atomic bomb effort, apparently did not feel that "we should
not need the Russians" until he had heard of the successful
Alamogordo test. It was also clear to him that only then had
the United States also changed its attitude regarding Russian
participation in the Japanese conflict. British consent "in
principle" to use the bomb was given on July 4, just before
the test.

Even many scientists, although quite confident of success
at this late date, reserved final judgment until the test at
Alamogordo on July 16, 1945.

If the Soviets had been fortunate enough, in the Yalta
period, to have received precise data on the U.S. atomic bomb
program, they might not have been impressed. At the end of
1944, General Groves, who was in charge of the U.S. Manhattan Project, informed the Chief of Staff and the President
that of the two types of weapons being manufactured, the
one having the greatest explosive power (10,000 tons of TNT
equivalent) would be ready about August 1, 1945, but the
production rate was such that another five months would
elapse before another bomb could be ready. This is a bomb
of impressive size, but the production rate at that time was
certainly unimpressive. No planners, either Soviet or American, could have anticipated in January 1945 that Japanese
resistance could have been broken six or seven months later
by a single atomic bomb of this size or with a few more of
much smaller size.

Of the atomic bomb that was expected to have a much smaller yield (500 tons of TNT equivalent), General Groves advised the Army Chief of Staff on December 30, 1944: "Our previous hopes that an implosion (compression) type bomb might be developed in the late spring have now been dissipated by scientific difficulties which we have not as yet been able to solve."[8] In fact, the chief explosive expert at Los Alamos was of the opinion that the project scientists were mad to think that such an absurd principle would work.

Stalin's technical advisers, if they had this information, might well have questioned whether, granted that the difficulties might be solved, the possession of a few 500-ton bombs with a radius of destruction less than four times that of conventional 10-ton blockbusters (which were relatively plentiful in supply) was worth the gigantic American effort.* Actually, the difficulties were overcome and the December 1944 expectations of yield were far exceeded, but this was the technical situation as it appeared at that time.

The knowledge acquired, then, at Yalta, combined with intelligence data about the progress of the American atomic energy program as of early 1945 (if, as is probable, the data were accurate), would have led rational Russian policymakers to conclude (1) that there was considerable uncertainty as to whether the United States was on the verge of achieving an atomic weapon of significant explosive strength and (2) that, in any event, the United States would not possess any significant number of such weapons in the foreseeable future.

---

* The radii of destruction of two sizes of bombs (whether they be of the conventional or atomic type) are proportionate to the cube roots of their energies. Thus, the radius of destruction of a 500-ton bomb exceeds that of a 10-ton bomb by a factor of the cube root of 50, or 3.7. The relative *areas* of destruction can be compared by squaring this latter value, which gives a ratio of 13.6.

7

HIROSHIMA AND THE KREMLIN

The contention that President Roosevelt talked with Stalin at Teheran in November 1943 about the atomic bomb project cannot be verified and is considered improbable.[1] It was at Teheran that Stalin gave his first promise to participate in the war against Japan *after* the defeat of Germany,[2] but it was much too early for the United States to have considered the employment of atomic weapons in that phase. There is no record of conversation about the atomic bomb at Teheran. It should be noted, however, that on at least one occasion—November 30, 1943—Roosevelt was in private contact with Marshal Stalin,[3] but presumably there was an interpreter present, who might have been a Russian interpreting for both Roosevelt and Stalin. It seems unlikely that Roosevelt mentioned the atomic bomb project, but the question remains open.

The first known opportunity to gauge the official Soviet attitude toward atomic energy on the eve of the atomic age

seemed to present itself when President Truman announced
to Stalin at Potsdam that "we have an entirely novel form of
bomb, something quite out of the ordinary, which we think
will have decisive effects upon the Japanese will to continue
the war."[4] But Stalin did not allow the opportunity to develop. His response was enigmatic. There are varying nar-
ratives, as reported by Churchill, Byrnes, and others, of the
manner in which Stalin received the news, all of which, of
course, were derived from Truman's own account. The most
important element of Truman's interpretation of Stalin's
reaction is that the latter did not understand the significance
of what he had been told.

It is probable that at this time Stalin had not independently received the results of the highly successful test of the
atomic bomb at Alamogordo, New Mexico, eight days earlier.
The reported espionage transmission times on this event are
very slow. Klaus Fuchs did not pass on this information until
September 1945 and the Canadian spy network did not trans-
mit data on this event to Moscow until August 9, 1945. There
is, of course, the possibility that other sources, still unknown,
were able to inform Moscow immediately. Earlier, in June,
the Russians had been advised by Fuchs that the test would
take place in July, so other agents could have been alerted.
Whatever the status of Stalin's information, it is possible he
did not understand that the new explosive was derived from
atomic nuclear forces, or that he knew nothing about atomic
energy at that time, or that he had concluded or been advised
beforehand that the American atomic bomb program had no
significant military importance. In any of these cases, Stalin's
failure to see great importance in the new American weapon
would reflect the Soviet government's official attitude toward
atomic energy as of July 1945.

Another interesting possibility remains. Stalin may have
believed that the United States had developed the bomb

solely as a threat and would never actually use the weapon in warfare. Thus his remark to President Truman that he (Stalin) "hoped we would use it" may have been ironic and derisive.

If this was indeed Stalin's belief, his convictions may have been strengthened by assurances from such scientists as Kapitsa that his Western colleagues would strongly advise the U.S. military against the actual use of the bomb on Japan. Indeed, this was somewhat the case, for a poll of 150 scientists at the University of Chicago in early June 1945 indicated a strong preference that the bomb be *demonstrated* to Japan rather than employed directly against her. In other words, a significant number, but by no means all, of the scientists polled urged that the bomb be used solely as a threat weapon.[5,6,7]

This revulsion at the possible use of the atomic weapon was not confined to scientists. General Eisenhower expressed his feelings on being told about the bomb just before it was tested: "I expressed the hope that we would never have to use such a thing against any enemy because I disliked seeing the United States take the lead in introducing into war something as horrible and destructive as this new weapon was described to be."[8]

Thus it is not unlikely that Stalin considered the atomic bomb to be only a threat weapon and felt that the Western powers would never permit its actual use. Stalin may have been profoundly surprised at the actual dropping of the bomb on Japan, and this could explain the almost hysterical Russian press reaction that followed.

Stalin's personal opinion on the imminence of the end of the Pacific War would also have affected his attitude when the bomb was finally dropped on Japan. The actual considerations that led to the employment of the weapon against Japan were described by Henry L. Stimson in his well-known

article in *Harper's Magazine* (February 1946). Articles and
books highly critical of the decision are numerous and are
based mainly on the contention of the United States Strategic Bombing Survey that

. . . certainly prior to 31 December 1945, and in all probability prior to 1 November 1945, Japan would have sur-
rendered even if the atomic bombs had not been dropped,
even if Russia had not entered the war, and even if no invasion had been planned or contemplated.

There is little doubt that the decision to surrender had
been made by the so-called "peace group" within the Japanese government long before the bombing of Hiroshima and
Nagasaki.[9,10] The atomic bomb served to catalyze their efforts; and again in the words of a less quoted section of the
Strategic Bombing Survey:

The atomic bombing considerably speeded up these political maneuverings within the government. . . . It is apparent
that in the atomic bomb the Japanese found the opportunity
which they had been seeking to break the existing deadlock
within the government over the acceptance of the Potsdam
terms.

Whether or not the atomic bombings did hasten the end
of the war and obviate the necessity of a large-scale invasion,
costly in lives, will always remain a matter of conjecture.
Nevertheless, at the time, there seemed to U.S. planners (and
to the British) to be compelling and valid reasons for the
employment of the atomic bomb against Japan. And Stalin
himself, if he understood what he was referring to, encouraged its use, perhaps facetiously.

Of more importance, and susceptible to more conclusive
interpretation, is the fact that neither Stalin nor any other
Russian ever officially approached the United States with a
request for more information about atomic energy. This
omission was probably one of the most significant indicators,
as of August 1945, of future Soviet intentions with respect

to atomic policy. Unless they had been deeply concerned about the role of the atomic bomb, it would not have been probable for the Russians to approach the Americans on that subject before they were officially notified of our atomic energy program, that is, at the earliest, July 24, 1945; to have made inquiries before that date might have revealed that the Soviet espionage system had been penetrating the Manhattan District. Because the American determination to keep the secret was soon afterwards made public in such unequivocal terms, the time period within which the Russians might conceivably have made official overtures was short. At the outside, the period could not have extended past October 8 when President Truman told reporters that "the United States would not give away its engineering 'know-how' which produced the atomic bomb to any nation."[11] The period was in fact probably much shorter, namely from July 24 to August 6. For on the latter date the President, in his public statement regarding the bomb just dropped on Hiroshima, said:

It has never been the habit of the scientists of this country or the policy of this Government to withhold from the world scientific knowledge. Normally, therefore, everything about the work with atomic energy would be made public. But under present circumstances it is not intended to divulge the technical processes of production or all the military applications, pending further examination of possible methods of protecting us and the rest of the world from the danger of sudden destruction.[12]

On returning to the United States several days later, Truman, in an address to the nation, reported on the Berlin Conference. In this address he stated:

The atomic bomb is too dangerous to be loose in a lawless world. That is why Great Britain and the United States, who have the secret of its production, do not intend to reveal the secret until means have been found to control the bomb so as to protect ourselves and the rest of the world from the danger of total destruction.[13]

Although it is certain that by this time the Russians had already embarked on a clearly discernible policy of isolation and hostility toward the capitalist world, these statements of the President of the United States could only have confirmed in their minds one of the reasons that had led them to adopt this intransigent policy. In accordance with communist doctrine, the capitalist world must by inexorable laws of history attempt to encircle and destroy the socialist state. Moreover, the Kremlin would think, the capitalists clearly perceived the communists' intentions regarding the overthrow of the capitalist system. In this context, what nation would the Russians think that Truman had in mind when he twice expressed concern about sharing atomic secrets lest the United States and the rest of the world suffer destruction? No other country in the world at that time except the Soviet Union had both the capacity and the freedom to utilize atomic secrets for military purposes. The identity of the power thus singled out for distrust must have been even more apparent to the Russians when these official statements were made within a few days after the Potsdam Conference, at which the most important questions affecting the postwar world were supposed to have been discussed and at which all three participants were supposed to have been considered equal in power, prestige, and trustworthiness. But the atomic bomb had not been put on the agenda, and Truman's colloquy with Stalin on the subject had not suggested the awesome international import of atomic energy that was expressed in official U.S. statements two weeks afterward.

Yet even if the Russians had not been given such clear indications that the United States would not be receptive to Soviet inquiries about atomic energy, there are several factors that probably would have influenced their decision to assume an air of incuriosity regarding the subject. During the war they had requested from the United States small quantities of uranium and heavy water "for research purposes." These requests may actually have been delicate feelers concerning American willingness to share officially the atomic secrets that were being shared unwittingly via Fuchs and others. In any event, the wariness with which American officials received these requests must have demonstrated to the Russians that the United States did not intend to give them access to that area of military secrets.

It is also probable that the Russians knew about the friction that had developed between the United States and Great Britain in 1943 over the sharing of atomic secrets, and the Russians were less likely than the British to perceive the distinction that U.S. officials were making between industrial and military secrets. They would, however, readily sense the difference between Great Britain and themselves with respect to the amount of trust that the United States would exercise in this field.

Klaus Fuchs would have been aware of this development, if only because the security regulations imposed by the Manhattan District in May 1943 partially cut off the flow of information to him because of his British citizenship. It is a fact that he was likely to have reported to the Russians. Whether or not he reported this in 1943 is not a matter of public record, but in September 1945 he did report to a Soviet agent that "there was no longer open and free and easy cooperation between the British and the Americans at Los Alamos and that many departments which had been formerly readily accessible to him were now closed."[14]

A clear indication of U.S. intentions to continue secrecy occurred in the spring of 1945. Among the recipients of an invitation to the 220th anniversary celebration of the Academy of Sciences of the Soviet Union were a group of American nuclear physicists. Several of these accepted the invitation at first, but later declined or did not arrive in Moscow.

The complete nonrepresentation of American nuclear physicists must have inhibited any Soviet scientist who might otherwise have urged his political superiors to attempt to obtain an exchange of information on nuclear energy with his American counterparts.

The late Dr. Irving Langmuir of the General Electric Company, who attended the 220th anniversary session of the Soviet Academy of Sciences, later commented on the denial of passports to physicists in testimony to the Special Senate Committee on Atomic Energy. (Of course, Soviet wartime atomic espionage activities had not yet been disclosed.) Dr. Langmuir was a Nobel Laureate. More Nobel prize winners were invited but did not attend, including Albert Einstein, Ernest O. Lawrence, Carl D. Anderson, and others of similar stature. Langmuir said:

I had had only a trivial connection with the atomic bomb in some consultations I had at two of the laboratories during 1942 or 1943. I had been invited to Russia in May 1945, had accepted through the Soviet Embassy, had received my passport, and was told that the American delegation would be taken to Russia on a C-54 plane with transportation arranged by the State Department and by the President. The day before we were scheduled to leave two Army officers, who did not know on what grounds the request was based, asked me to decline to go to Russia. This would have meant that I would have had to invent excuses on my own responsibility. Since there appeared to be direct conflict between the War Department and the State Department, I refused to withdraw my acceptance at the request of the War Department and demanded that the matter be taken up with the State Department cancelling my passport if necessary. I wholly disapproved of the manner in which this matter was handled. When others interceded and the War Department was made to realize how little I knew of the atomic energy project, I was finally allowed to go.

Other Americans, however, who had been invited, were not permitted to go after having accepted.

This, of course, the Russian Embassy knew. They knew also that no physicists were among those who accepted the invitations.

When I reached Russia I was told by the English group that eight British physicists who had accepted the Russian invitation, had had their passports cancelled after they had reached the airport ready to fly to Moscow. All of the scientists and the whole of the British delegation were much incensed at these tactics. They believed that the passports were cancelled because these men had worked on the Tuballoy Project which is the equivalent of our Manhattan Project. I also heard the opinion expressed that this action must have been taken at the request of the American Government because no one outside of the American Army could be so stupid.

The English newspapers gave great publicity to the cancellation of the passports and called Prime Minister Churchill to account before the House of Commons. This was all known in Russia, but it was never published in American newspapers.

I believe that these attempts to maintain secrecy resulted in giving to the Russians the very information which the Army most wished to keep from them. Any sensible Russian scientist knowing of these facts would have believed that we were developing an atomic bomb and were keeping it secret from the Russians.[15]

There also may have been something in the manner of President Truman's July 24 announcement to Stalin that the latter would have interpreted as convincing evidence that the United States had no intention of sharing atomic secrets. It is reliably reported that Truman later said that he formulated his communication to Stalin in such a way as to reveal the minimum amount of information.* Stalin, particularly

---

* See, for example, Churchill's *Triumph and Tragedy*, pp. 640–41: "He [Truman] reiterated his resolve at all costs to refuse to divulge any particulars. . . . 'I think,' he said, 'I had best just tell him [Stalin] after one of our meetings that we have an entirely novel form of bomb, something quite out of the ordinary, which we think will have decisive effects upon the Japanese will to continue the war.' "

if he had been briefed about atomic energy beforehand, may have been keenly aware of this fact; he certainly would have been reminded of it when the bomb was dropped on Hiroshima. Another attitude influencing decision in this matter would have been a feeling of inferiority, a reluctance to admit openly that Soviet science was lagging behind American science in this field; this attitude would not necessarily affect the Soviet scientist, but would be decisive with the Soviet politician.

Curiously, at this same time—the spring of 1945—Soviet censorship on atomic energy eased somewhat for a period of several months. Some Soviet work that had been kept secret in 1943 and 1944 (but certainly not all of it) appeared in the scientific press. In fact, some of the papers published in the Soviet scientific press in May and June of 1945 discussed subjects that were then highly classified in the United States and Great Britain. But this temporary ease-up applied only to certain laboratory techniques and basic theory rather than to any work directly relating to the engineering of a large-scale atomic program.

The slackening of Soviet classification, coming at this time, may have been part of a cautious feeler effort toward the loosening of U.S. controls on atomic information. Perhaps the hope was that Western scientists, after seeing Soviet information of the type that they themselves were not permitted to publish, would pressure their governments to release some of the closely held atomic information. Also, it might have been the beginning of an attempt to establish the Soviet Union as a world equal in atomic research. The cold water that U.S. statesmen threw on the sharing of atomic information right after Hiroshima may have had the additional effect of closing the slowly opening door of the Soviet atomic program. By the fall of 1945, Soviet atomic classification policies had become even more rigid than those of the United States.

Regarding the immediate reaction of the Kremlin leaders when the bomb was dropped on Hiroshima on August 6, 1945, there is little record. Stanislaw Mikolajczyk, of the Polish Provisional Government, was at Moscow at this time, engaged in reparations talks with Soviet leaders. He reports:

> I was staying in Moscow at the time of the dropping of the atom bomb on Hiroshima. I got the news of this event from the American Embassy in Moscow. It made a terrific impression on me. I knew of the fear with which the Allies observed German work on the creation of an atom bomb from heavy water, and how much effort the Allies expended in the destruction of the plants manufacturing heavy water in Norway. I was well aware of the universal fear—especially in view of the announcement of the impending use of a new weapon by Hitler—lest the Germans, coming at last to the possession of the atomic bomb, alter the course of the war at the very last moment. For this reason, the news that the Allies possess the bomb and have used it for the first time made a great impression on me.
>
> So I asked Mr. Modzelewski, the Polish Vice-Minister of Foreign Affairs, whom, along with Messrs. Bierut and Minc, I knew had been received the night before at the Kremlin by Stalin and Molotov, what he thinks of the subject, and what effects it would have on the development of the international situation.
>
> Unhesitatingly, he gave a ready answer—this is the usual American propaganda, it has no significant military meaning, and has as its single purpose the rapid forcing of the Soviets into the Japanese war with which the Americans are having difficulty.
>
> The following evening we were all at supper with Molotov. I repeated again my question. Molotov answered: "This is American propaganda. From a military point of view it has no important meaning whatsoever."[16]

General Eisenhower arrived at Moscow on August 11, 1945, for extensive conversations with Stalin and Soviet military leaders on military matters. It is interesting that neither Eisenhower nor the U.S. Military Attaché at Moscow at that time reported any mention at all of the atomic bomb in these conversations. This was at a time when the atomic bomb overshadowed all other military considerations and at a time when Eisenhower himself recalled that "the reports that reached us after the first one was used at Hiroshima in August left no doubt in our minds that a new era of warfare had begun."[17]

Clearly the above shows that in this early period the official Russian attitude was to ignore and minimize the importance of the atomic bomb.

The foreign Communist press exhibited lack of instructions from Moscow. The day after the Hiroshima drop, the *London Daily Worker* wrote: "The appliance of the new weapon on a large scale should hasten the surrender of Japan. The new discovery will save precious lives for the Allies." And more effusively after the second bomb was dropped on Nagasaki, the *Worker* stated: "The use of the atomic bomb was an act of charity because it shortened the war and saved human lives."

Meanwhile the Vatican had expressed discontent over the use of the bomb, and the Paris *Humanité* expressed indignation toward the Holy See for that attitude. And in Rome, the Communist voice *L'Unità* argued in an editorial entitled "On the Service of Civilization" that condemnation of the atomic bomb is "a peculiar psychological and doctrinaire deviation, a submission to a certain kind of abstract humanitarianism." A few weeks later, after Moscow had defined the proper course of of humanitarianism, all Communist spokesmen promptly submitted and deviated the required one hundred and eighty degrees. To quote the *Daily Worker* again, for example, on the seventh anniversary of the Hiroshima bombing: "The excuse that in the long run this bestial action saves lives is valueless. Each time during the war when a crime was committed such an excuse was used to justify it."

The first blast at the monopoly of the "secret" came in the propaganda journal *New Times* just a few weeks after the atomic bombs had been dropped at Hiroshima and Naga-saki: "The American reactionary press insists that the United States must keep the method of production of atomic bombs a secret in the expectation of future war." The writer was Modest Rubinstein, one of the Soviet Union's most prolific propagandists specializing in technical and military affairs (and an official observer of the 1956 U.S. elections). Rubin-stein then warned that the secret could not remain for long the monopoly of any single nation. This article established the tone—or rather the monotone—of Soviet public policy for the postwar period.

The Rubinstein article also typified the "double-think" nature of Soviet policy toward the peaceful uses of atomic energy. Faced with the problem of showing that the develop-ment of benign applications of atomic energy was incom-patible with the American capitalistic system but was the logical course of events in the communist system, Rubinstein fabricated a unique theory:

If atomic energy is applied on a big scale to industry, it would, owing to the predominance of capitalistic monopoly, result in stupendous unemployment, in the permanent displace-ment of millions of miners and other workers, and in further enhancing the power of the monopolies, not to mention the awful peril involved if this formidable weapon should fall into the hands of the aggressors.[18]

Here was a genuine plea, couched in the familiar Marxist-Leninist terms, to share the "secrets" of the atom for the good of mankind, as interpreted by the Soviet Union.

Then, in November, on the 28th Anniversary of the Bolshevik Revolution, Foreign Minister Molotov further pounded the theme of "monopoly of atomic secrets":

. . . it is necessary to speak of the discovery of atomic energy and about the atomic bomb, the use of which in the war with

Japan showed its great destructive power. Atomic energy, however, has not been explored as a means of preventing aggression or for the purpose of preserving peace. On the other hand, nowadays there can be no technological secrets of this magnitude that can remain the possession of some single country or of some narrow group of countries. Therefore, the discovery of atomic energy must not encourage either enthusiasm concerning the utilization of this discovery for external political play of forces, or irresponsibility concerning the future of peace-loving peoples. In our era of high technical achievements and of wide application of science in production, when it has already become possible to utilize atomic energy and other great technical discoveries, in the economic plans the main attention must be devoted to questions of raising the technical level of our industries, and to the creation of highly qualified ranks of technical people. We must equal the achievements of the contemporary world in all the branches of industry and national economy. We must secure conditions for a world-wide movement forward of Soviet science and technology. The enemy interfered with our peaceful, creative work. But we will catch up on what we must and we will achieve the flowering of our nation. We will have atomic energy also, and much else. [Tumultuous and prolonged applause. Everyone rises.] Let us tackle the solution of these problems with all our inexhaustible bolshevik energy, with all that mighty energy of the Soviet people. So let us work as our comrade Stalin taught us. [Tumultuous applause.][19]

The following issue of *Krokodil*, the Soviet "humor" magazine, bore on the cover a colorful illustration of two parents, John Bull (as the mother) and Uncle Sam (as the father) doting over an invisible baby in a blue pram. (Of course, her coverlet is an American flag with "Atomic Energy" embroidered on it.) A bystander asks: "How do you intend to bring up your youngster?" The parents reply: "In a strictly private boarding school."

The story was echoed in the United Nations by Gromyko: "The discovery of methods of using atomic energy cannot remain for an indefinite time the property of only one country or small group of countries" (June 18, 1946). Molotov later put it more strongly, declaring that the Baruch plan for the international control of atomic energy "unfortunately suffers from a certain amount of egoism. It proceeds from the desire to secure for the United States of America the monopolistic possession of the atomic bomb" (October 29, 1946).

On September 24, 1946, Stalin himself said: "Of course, the monopolistic possession of the secret of the atom bomb creates a menace, but against this there are at least two remedies: (a) the monopolistic possession of the atom bomb cannot last long; (b) the use of the atom bomb will be prohibited."

Probably the last opportunity for the Russians to officially raise the question of sharing atomic information before official U.S. policy on this matter was solidified was at the London Conference of the Council of Foreign Ministers, September 11 to October 2, 1945. (So far as officially enunciated policy is concerned, the appropriate date in this connection is probably October 3, 1945, when President Truman presented his Message to Congress on Atomic Energy.) This was the first meeting of the body formed by a protocol of the Potsdam Conference "to do the necessary preparatory work for the peace settlements." Since another clause stated that "other matters may from time to time be referred to the Council by agreement between the member Governments," the Russians presumably had latitude to ask that atomic energy be put on the agenda. At least they could have taken the opportunity of daily contact with Americans to discuss the matter informally. But they did neither. Mr. Byrnes wrote:

At Moscow, as at Potsdam and then at the Council of Foreign Ministers meeting in London, no member of the Soviet delegation expressed any curiosity about atomic energy. At Potsdam, neither Stalin nor Molotov had mentioned the matter after the President's talk with the Generalissimo. At London, Mr. Molotov showed no interest whatever; his only references to the bomb were a few offhand remarks about my carrying an atomic bomb in my pocket.[20]

Molotov's remarks seem to indicate that he already had formulated in his mind the concept of "U.S. atomic diplomacy" that in later years became one of the principal elements in the Soviet opposition to U.S. atomic policy.

Mr. Byrnes' next sentence is: "I decided that I was right in the conclusion I had come to at Potsdam, that the Russians never disclose information about such a discovery to anyone else and so thought it would be improper for them to exhibit curiosity about ours." As the argument in the above pages makes clear, it is believed that factors other than a question of propriety motivated the Russians.

At any rate, at an "unusual press conference" at Realfoot Lake, Tennessee, President Truman, a few days after the London Conference, made it clear to the Russians that they could expect no cooperation at all in either the industrial or military aspects of atomic energy. According to *The New York Times* of October 9, 1945, the President said:

. . . the United States would not give away its engineering "know-how" which produced the atomic bomb to any nation. He said that the information would be useless to any other country anyway, since only the United States had the combination of industrial capacity and resources necessary to produce the bomb. The President added that this position of the U.S. Government had not been discussed with Great Britain or Canada as partners in the development of the atomic bomb, but he was confident their view would be the same as that of the United States.

Although Britain and Canada had the blueprint of the atomic bomb secret, they would be unable to apply the knowledge for lack of plant facilities, the President said.

Of the knowledge which came out of the $2 billion wartime experiment, Mr. Truman said in answer to questions at a press conference that that was our business and others would just have to catch up with us.

Asked whether Russia might not eventually be able to acquire the engineering skill as well as develop the resources and industrial capacity needed for processing the bomb, the President said that the questioner's guess was as good as his.

The public minimization of the effects of the atomic bomb was the most immediate postwar reaction, for it directly concerned the credit that the Soviet Union desired in terminating the Pacific War. An early *Izvestiia* commentary complained:

Certain American newspapers try to minimize the Soviet Union's contribution to the common Allied cause. The *New York Daily News* boasted a few days ago: "We have won the war with the atomic bomb."

We recollect the statement made by Lord Louis Mountbatten, Commander-in-Chief of the Allied Forces in Southeast Asia, at a press conference held in London on August 9. He said then that it would be the greatest stupidity to think that the atomic bomb could put an end to the war.

The war could not have been concluded by any sensational miracles, but only by the powerful joint efforts of all the Allies who struck at Hitler Germany and Imperial Japan.[21]

Actually, placed in this context, the *Izvestiia* comment is a distortion of Lord Mountbatten's statement. He had simply emphasized that as a commander it was his responsibility to continue his operations

notwithstanding the effect of the atomic bomb and the Soviet Union's entry into the Pacific War. A commander's job is to go on planning operations and keep up the greatest pressure against the enemy. It would be the greatest folly if I should work on the assumption that the atomic bomb will stop the war.[22]

A Soviet military observer, Colonel M. Tolchenov, in an article in the internationally circulated *New Times,* brought forth all the ammunition he could collect to establish the importance of Russia's entry into the Pacific War. For to the Kremlin leaders their first concern over the atomic weapon was the possibility that it might exclude the Russians from sharing what they believed was their portion of the spoils of the Pacific War.

Another deep-seated Russian attitude would have pervaded the Kremlin's approach to the question of seeking atomic secrets openly from the West; this was the complex national feeling of inferiority. One of the most embittering wounds that could be inflicted on this kind of sensitivity, and the kind that would be expected to cause a reaction of withdrawal, would be disaparagement or lack of recognition by foreigners of Russian achievement in fields where they were actually well advanced or even superior. As we have seen, the Russians seem to have been at least equal with the West in nuclear physics at the time when the United States and Great Britain decided to develop atomic energy at a greatly accelerated tempo. But the Kapitsas and the Kurchatovs of Russia were not invited to join the Manhattan District Project, while the British were.

Through inadvertence, in public statements after the war, the United States continued to ignore the Soviet prewar achievements in nuclear physics. For example, a statement by the U.S. Secretary of War on August 6, 1945, said: "Until 1939 work in this field was world-wide, being carried on particularly in the United States, the United Kingdom, Germany, France, Italy and Denmark." This omission to acknowledge earlier Soviet pre-eminence in nuclear physics, despite a rather extensive Soviet literature on the subject, is not likely to have been interpreted by the Russians as due only to lack of information, particularly since the Russians seem to grant skill and diligence to the American intelligence system. It may have been interpreted by them as a calculated move to deceive the masses of the Western world regarding Soviet potential in this field, an opinion that would be a necessary part of the United States policy of "atomic diplomacy" as viewed by the Russians. But insult was probably nevertheless inferred.

Pervading all of the above factors and probably more decisive than any single one of them must have been the abhorrence of intimate relationships with foreigners that was so characteristic of at least the Stalinist period of the Soviet regime. This attitude is apparently complex and not explainable solely in terms of extreme sensitivity about revealing Soviet secrets—though this would necessarily have been involved if Soviet nuclear physicists were permitted to consult with American scientists. It reached its nearly pathological peak of expression in the subsequent campaigns that have been designated "priority in inventions" and "cosmopolitanism" and became formalized in one of its aspects in the legal decree on the preservation of secrets in June 1947.

All these factors were at play within a general political climate that at the very end of the war cast a heavy shadow on the prospects for American-Soviet cooperation in any field. It is not within the scope of this book to analyze the origins of the cold war. But for an understanding of the immediate postwar Soviet attitude toward atomic energy, it is necessary to point out that the dissolution of the wartime alliance between the Soviet Union and the West had begun at least several months before it was appropriate for the USSR to take any public position regarding atomic energy. Moreover, immediately following the surrender of Germany in May 1945, there had been a perceptible shift in Soviet attitude toward the Western Allies from the wartime expedient interest in limited cooperation to poorly disguised competition over prospective postwar settlements.

Regardless of motivations, the failure of the Russians offi-

cially to seek an exchange of information with the United
States had far-reaching consequences whether or not they
foresaw them at the time. Since the tempo of growth of conflict between the USSR and the West increased sharply after
the autumn of 1945, there was never subsequently as propitious a time to take such action. Therefore the isolation
in atomic matters decided on by the USSR in August 1945
was irrevocable. Three important results followed:

1. The principal inducement in the American plan for
international control of atomic energy—that the ultimate
reward to nations joining the proposed International Atomic
Development Authority would be sharing all the American
knowledge about atomic energy—was not attractive to the
Russians. Therefore, the American proposal to the United
Nations was doomed to failure several months before it was
formulated. All thoughtful analyses of the Russian position
regarding atomic energy in the United Nations have cor-
rectly stressed the deprivations in the stipulated early stages
of the Baruch Plan as being unacceptable to the Russians.
It is suggested here that the benefits offered by the plan were
worthless in the Russian view, and that their failure to seek
these "benefits" in July–August 1945 constituted advance
notice of their indifference.

2. A precedent was firmly set whereby Soviet scientists
would pursue an independent path in atomic research in the
postwar period.

3. The Russians laid the groundwork for an atomic arms
race with the United States. In doing so, they were apparently not farsighted. Evidently, they foresaw a time when
they too would have atomic weapons, but they showed no
concern until several years later over the re-examination
that this would entail of the structure of their military establishment and of their Marxian calculations of the nature
and balance of the forces that control society.

8

THE SCIENTISTS RENEW
THEIR EFFORTS

By the fourth quarter of 1943, the Moscow workers of the Academy of Sciences were able to return to their laboratories from their scattered temporary posts in Alma-Ata, Krasnoyarsk, *et cetera*. The leading Soviet nuclear physicist, Igor Kurchatov, also came to Moscow and apparently never returned to his original laboratory, the Nuclear Physics Laboratory of the Leningrad Physico-Technical Institute.

Earlier that year—in August—Kurchatov was the subject of an article in *Izvestiia* that praised him in the highest possible terms. The author of the article was Abram Ioffe, dean of Soviet science. A month later, Kurchatov was awarded a full membership in the Academy of Sciences of the USSR.

This brief burst of public glory just preceded the lowering of the curtain of silence around Kurchatov and the Soviet atomic program. At the same session of the Academy of Sciences that elected Kurchatov, the recorded report on the scientific work in 1942 and the first six months of 1943 contained no mention of specific atomic energy research. But the subject had always received attention in reports for 1941 and previous years. This omission was to be expected on two counts: (1) comparatively little work had been done in those eighteen months, and (2) the secrecy curtain had finally fallen on atomic energy.

Evidently, when preparation was made for this General Session of 1943, atomic energy had been considered, and it was decided to give the delegates in open session only a brief precautionary statement: "The problem of the atomic nucleus now attracts the urgent attention of scientists of the entire world and it is not necessary to discuss it further," said Aleksandr Baikov, in outlining the scientific plan for 1944.[1]

Note particularly the terse indication of the urgency of the problem and the thinly veiled admonition that the subject was no longer to be discussed.

The prominent Soviet physicist, Yakov I. Frenkel, indicated in the summer of 1943 a revived interest in the subject:

Four years ago, when a newspaperman asked Einstein a question about the prospects of technical utilization of atomic energy, he answered: "One may as well throw bricks at crows by night."
The development of nuclear physics during the past two or three years has somewhat shaken this pessimistic point of view and has again winged physicists with the hope of solving the problem of transmutation of atoms on an industrial scale.[2]

In the realm of future theoretical work on the atomic nucleus, Frenkel had many speculations to offer. He allowed his imagination to roam so far that he checked himself: "Here, however, we overstep the limits of contemporary physical science at the risk of falling into the realm of unscientific fantasy." But he concluded his article on a hopeful and free note:

On the other hand, the past history of the development of physics shows how limited and narrow were our notions about the physical world until quite recently. In discussing problems of contemporary physics, we must therefore not be afraid, even when scientific method of proof does not yet fully justify it, to expand the boundaries of physics.[3]

At about the same time (May 18, 1943) Kapitsa also reiterated his earlier interest in the atom:

The direction in which the Institute [his own Institute of Physical Problems] develops must correspond to that direction of science which is most promising at the moment, and which, taking into consideration the present state of science and the methodological possibilities, has the widest prospects for rapid and fruitful progress.

In the sphere of physics there are, in my view, three such fundamental directions: research in low temperatures, *research in the atomic nucleus,* and finally, the solid body [italics supplied].[4]

Apparently, excitement ran high in some quarters; the previously mentioned booklet (in "The Dormant Period," Chapter 5) by Kolman reflects this. The author is a Marxian theoretician, a "philosopher" of science. But within the limitations of his subject matter, he is rather sober and factual. The almost lyrical paragraphs with which he ends the booklet are therefore striking by contrast. They seem to reflect an enthusiasm that must have been prevalent in the scientific community:

Our Soviet physics has contributed and is contributing a significant share in the great task of finally achieving victory over the sworn enemy—Fascism. And when the great hour of triumph of our just cause arrives, Soviet physics, strengthened by strenuous labor, having served the lofty cause of preserving the very existence of science itself, will with mighty force, daring, and skill born of experience, take by storm the most complex theoretical problems of modern physics, the physics of the atomic world. Advancing in the first rank of

world science, Soviet physics will seize one fortress after
another, never halting, striding ever forward.

For though in our acquisition of scientific knowledge we
constantly master new fundamental truths, we can never
exhaust it or understand the ultimate; for nature is infinite,
infinitely diverse and infinitely changing. Indeed, the fasci-
nation and magnificence of science lies in the fact that it
can never be satisfied with the state of knowledge; that any
goal achieved always opens up still more majestic perspectives for the future.

At first glance one might guess that in the spring of 1943
the thoughts of Soviet scientists were turning to atomic energy
because the victory at Stalingrad had made certain the turning point in the war had been reached and, therefore, scientists might look forward to returning to work that had been
abandoned because of a desperate and uncertain conflict.
But only a few months earlier another momentous event had
occurred. On December 2, 1942, at the University of Chicago,
Enrico Fermi had achieved the world's first chain reaction,
and had, as the culmination of three years' labor, shown the
possibility of "transmutation of atoms on an industrial scale."
Indeed, until this time, it was not at all certain that a nuclear
chain reaction could be achieved. This raises the question,
impossible of proof: *Did the December 2, 1942, chain reaction serve as a catalyst for both the U.S. and the Soviet
atomic projects?*

In any event, a report in the autumn of 1943 by Aleksandr
Y. Fersman, the foremost Soviet geologist, made it clear that
research in atomic energy had been resumed in the USSR:

Still timid attempts are made today to subdue the energy
of the atom. The tremendous energy pent up in matter does
not yet seem to all to be a real source of industrial power of
the future, and heated scientific debates are even taking place
about the unstable isotope of uranium. In all countries, perhaps particularly on account of the war, enormous research
work is being done in that direction. Eleven special labora-

tories are working on this problem in America, and in our own country too it is being widely investigated. Perhaps not so soon, and yet perhaps tomorrow it may supply humanity with an absolutely new and immeasurable source of energy.[5]

The most striking element in all of these statements about atomic energy is their exclusive concern with industrial and medicinal applications of atomic energy. In none of these speeches—with the possible exception of Baikov's—was there even a hint that it might be used for war. A few paragraphs from Frenkel's speech will underline this interesting fact:

Just before the war broke out, physicists throughout the world began applying themselves with unusual energy to the practical solution of the "uranium problem," i.e., to creating conditions necessary to obtain a chain reaction in splitting uranium. The most important problem was to separate its light isotope.

Solution of this problem would have opened to humanity quite unusual technical perspectives. It would have produced a new source of power a million times more advantageous (in quantity of power per given mass of substance) than coal or oil, though much less widespread (geologically).

Immediately after the war the problem of uranium will doubtless become the central focus in contemporary experimental and technical physics.

Simultaneously, the problem will be vigorously pursued of obtaining charged particles—nuclei of hydrogen and helium—with considerably higher energies than those attained thus far. America, where at the present time 18 powerful cyclotrons are working, just before the outbreak of the war began planning construction of a new gigantic cyclotron capable of imparting to charged particles energy of the order of 100 million volts.

At these potentials, the power factor of nuclear reactions . . . should increase many hundred, or perhaps many thousand, times, as compared with values attained thus far. Under such conditions it will be possible to conduct nuclear reactions not only in laboratories but on an industrial scale, especially if the purpose is not to use intra-atomic energy but to obtain valuable and rare elements by transmuting elements widely available in nature.

The great significance of these results in medical science is self-evident (not without reason do the largest American hospitals have their own powerful cyclotrons).

Concurrently, artificial radio elements have acquired unusually wide application in the form of "tracer atoms" or "indicators" in a variety of physical-chemical studies.[6]

Frenkel's obliviousness to the nature of the American program reveals either genuine ignorance of the espionage data about the Manhattan District or a remarkable guile.* For reasons adduced in Chapter 6, it is conceivable that he knew nothing of the details of the American program. But his implication that his own government would develop atomic energy solely for peaceful purposes involves an ingenuousness on his part that is more difficult to believe, particularly since Kapitsa's speech in 1941 revealed clearly that the use of atomic energy for military purposes was being debated by scientists. The most reasonable explanation is that Frenkel—and the others who spoke in the same vein— were not naïve, but were trying to advocate a special point of view. Perhaps at a time when a Soviet nuclear program was about to be launched, some scientists were making a last plea that it not be frozen into a military pattern. This may be the meaning of Frenkel's strongly implied preference for producing radioactive isotopes rather than releasing nuclear energy.

This emphasis on peaceful application of research findings in the nuclear field, completely excluding mention of possible military use, may have been a form of Aesopian language. By this device, the Soviet scientists who spoke may

* But Fersman did not seem to be so ill-informed when he said: "In all countries, *perhaps particularly on account of the war*, enormous research work is being done in that direction" [italics supplied]. (Fersman, *Les Sciences Naturelles en URSS depuis 25 ans.*)

have wanted to communicate to their Soviet colleagues (and to scientists abroad?) their deep-seated preference to see atomic energy placed in peaceful channels. They may also have wished to convey the same message to their own government, reinforcing by public statement what they may have been urging on politicians in private. This measure of defiance would still have been permissible under the conditions of relative scientific candor that existed in the Soviet Union in the middle of the war. Also, their statements may have been in part purposeless expressions of last-ditch wishful thinking.

In fact, there is the strong suggestion here that there may have been two or more opposing scientific camps in the Soviet Union. Fersman's conciliatory description of the American project and his reference to "heated scientific debates" indicate that in 1943 all had not been resolved on the direction that the Soviet atomic energy program should take. But Baikov's tight-lipped reference to atomic energy was in sharp contrast to the remarks of Fersman and Frenkel. Frenkel was speaking about hypothetical future atomic research, and probably at a time when the actual Soviet program had not yet been planned in detail. Baikov mentioned atomic energy in a very concrete context: he was describing the "Plan of Work of the Academy of Sciences of the USSR for 1944." His elliptical remark that "the significance of this problem [the atomic nucleus] needs no explanation" no doubt indicates that the Soviet security curtain had dropped. If a conflict had been waged on the issue of military *versus* peaceful orientation of an atomic program, Baikov may have been announcing in this manner its resolution. Baikov knew whereof he spoke, for in the implementation of the 1944 plan, Baikov was appointed Chairman of the Scientific Experts Council of the State Planning Commission of the USSR (Gosplan).

Baikov's own political position may be guessed from the tribute paid him in an article in the *Great Soviet Encyclopedia*. He was praised for combining theoretical and practical skills and for devoting them to the service of the Soviet State. This tribute is one of the highest that can be given in Stalinist language and is a rather certain indication that the political authorities considered Baikov's loyalty to be unquestioned. No such praise is given to the equally prominent Kapitsa in the article on him in the same encyclopedia.

The probable line-up of the two camps can be inferred. Kurchatov, having gone so far in his wartime service to his own government that he abandoned temporarily his promising researches in nuclear physics, would have been in the weapons camp. Kapitsa and his other elder colleagues such as Fersman and Frenkel would have opposed him. The politicians would have been strongly prejudiced in favor of advice given by Kurchatov, both because he had proved himself loyal and because his advice would correspond to their own preferences.

This issue, however, was not as simple and perhaps not as hotly debated as the above paragraphs might imply.

In the first place, the Soviet political authorities were apparently skeptical about the prospects for practical results to be derived from nuclear research within a foreseeable future. This attitude seemed to have persisted even after 1945. Therefore, if they did not consider the problem urgent, they would not have stimulated acrimony among scientists and insisted on a showdown as early as 1943 over a question about the ultimate uses to which scientific findings would be put. For one thing, if science should demonstrate that achievement of weapons was impracticable, the political leaders would still be interested in the possible industrial applications that might give the weak Soviet economy a much-needed boost.

In the second place, the program—from 1943 to 1945 at least—was on a relatively small scale and was preparatory in nature. While decidedly directed toward weapons as an end result, the program at this stage could later be steered in either direction without undue waste. In a sense, therefore, scientists, regardless of misapprehensions, could still hope that as the program developed, its course might change toward a peaceful direction.

Finally, the motivation to work in their field of primary interest is so strong among scientists that Soviet nuclear physicists would have willingly participated in a weapons-oriented program even though the objective would be distasteful to them.

But some physicists were adverse to participating in certain lines of weapons research that the government demanded; they were kept under surveillance, imprisoned, or exiled in the years between World War II and Stalin's death. With the information available, it is impossible at this time to assess the effect of the attitudes of these outspoken physicists on the Soviet atomic energy program, or indeed to know definitely whether they were rebellious or simply opposed on technical grounds to various approaches to weapons development.

It might be argued that Frenkel and others were speaking under instructions of their government to conceal the fact that a program of atomic research directed toward military ends was about to be launched. Such a line would be consistent with the postwar pretense of the Soviet government that its nuclear energy program was primarily peaceful in intent. Because of this, such an argument cannot be dismissed. But it seems unacceptable for the following reasons:

1. There is convincing evidence that the Soviet government was not concerned—even for a long period after the Hiroshima bombing—about an *immediate* necessity to cope

with an American atomic military capability. The Russians seemed to consider that this capability would become a reality only in a future more remote than it turned out to be. Therefore, if they were shortsighted with respect to this problem, it is not logical to assume that they would have been foresighted enough to conceal the military nature of an incipient atomic program of their own by the rather sophisticated device of advertising that a solely peacefully oriented program was about to begin. The Soviet program, from 1943 onward, was indeed surrounded in the utter secrecy of which only the Soviet Union is capable. But this policy is applied to any new Soviet weapon in the development stage.

2. After the autumn of 1943—when an atomic program aimed toward weapons was begun—and until the first Soviet atomic explosion in 1949, no public statement was made by any reputable Soviet scientist about *specific* and practicable plans for using atomic energy for industrial or medicinal purposes. Only politicians spoke of it in specific terms (blowing up mountains); scientists, when they spoke at all, employed generalities. Therefore, if Soviet political authorities did not consider it wise to compel their prominent physicists to emphasize atomic applications in the decade 1944–54, it is improbable that it was political prodding that led them to do so in the autumn of 1943.

3. The USSR was exhausted by the war from 1943 to at least 1948. It was in a relatively weak power position to support its political ambitions for a postwar rearrangement of the world—at least until American troops were demobilized and withdrawn from Europe and Asia. Therefore, if Soviet leaders had considered atomic energy an immediate military potentiality, they might have had a greater political advantage in stressing the fact that they began a militarily oriented atomic program in 1943 than in pretending that it would be applied solely to industry and medicine.

4. *After* Hiroshima, the "peaceful" line was much more advantageous to the USSR because of the stigma attached to the United States by that event, and because, after the war, the world was avid for peace. But the situation in 1943 was radically different. Then the Soviet Union would have gained more political advantage by emphasizing a *militarily* oriented, rather than a *peacefully* oriented, program. Probably it was the Stalinist obsession with military secrecy that prevented their doing either effectively.

9

THEIR FIRST CHAIN
REACTION

Once the decison had been made to pursue an intensive
atomic energy program, it was necessary to decide whether
to attempt the formidable task of separating the fissionable
isotope of uranium, U-235, from the more abundant isotope,
U-238; or to manufacture in nuclear reactors an artificially
created fissionable material, plutonium; or, for versatility,
to attempt both schemes. The United States had tackled both
programs with success—but the plutonium production process
was by far the simpler. It was logical for the Soviets to attempt the latter first. Any other general direction required
was provided by the Russian translation of the famous U.S.
Smyth Report, which went to press at Moscow in January
1946, with an initial printing of 30,000 copies.

Unfortunately, Soviet publications contain practically no
references to their uranium isotope separation program. Before the possibility of using plutonium was known, interest,
of course, was centered on the separation of uranium-235.

But from the earliest period, skeptical voices had been raised. In commenting on a major talk by Igor Kurchatov on "The Fission of Heavy Nuclei" at Moscow toward the end of 1940, Khariton remarked that "concerning the separation of the uranium isotopes it must be mentioned that the present method of separating the isotopes by thermo-diffusion requires energy of the same order as that gained in the chain reaction."[1] In other words, separation of U-235 seemed simply not economically feasible.

In late 1943, a period of decision in the Soviet atomic energy program, this skepticism persisted, for Fersman bluntly stated that "heated scientific debates are even taking place about the unstable isotope of uranium."

In May 1956, Kapitsa himself provided a clue to the status of the Soviet atomic energy program from 1943 to 1947. Kapitsa explained to a visiting group of distinguished American physicists that he had been put under house arrest by Beria in 1947 because of his refusal to work on the uranium separation program. On moral grounds, this was a rather puzzling attitude for Kapitsa to adopt. This was not a question of the size or use of a nuclear weapon (which prompted the "atomic" *versus* "hydrogen" bomb argument in the United States), but of the method of bomb production. It may well be that Kapitsa was strongly prejudiced against uranium isotope separation on the grounds of technical and economic feasibility.

Other stories have it that Kapitsa, who was never before loath to think about them, refused to work on nuclear weapons. Actually, the penalty for refusal to work on a project of the highest state priority would probably have resulted in something more drastic than house arrest. The actual cause is probably related to technical disagreements as noted above and, even more likely, to promises unfulfilled. An indication of the state of affairs in 1947 comes from Colonel G. A.

Tokaev, a Soviet jet and rocket expert who escaped to the West in 1948. He stated that "a number of specialists who had been working on atomic projects were arrested in 1947 for negligence and lack of results."[2] During that year, Beria took the matter in hand, and research work was in progress when on November 8, 1947, Molotov said that "the USSR knows the secret of the atom bomb."

It should be noted that the immediate postwar period was also the period when the U.S. isotope separation program underwent serious re-examination. Of the two major existing methods of separating the isotopes of uranium, one was abandoned, and no new facilities for the other process (gaseous diffusion) were built for a period of some two and one-half years after the U.S. Atomic Energy Commission was formed in early 1947. The technical and economic issues of uranium isotope separation had by no means been fully resolved by either the United States or the USSR in this crucial period. Also, it was not until the end of 1947 that the British decided to build a gaseous diffusion plant; this decision could have catalyzed the Soviet effort along the same lines.

Thus, the meager evidence available strongly suggests that 1947, when Kapitsa chanced Beria's disfavor, marks the beginning of this Soviet gaseous diffusion effort. Although, as we shall see, this was also an important year for the Soviet plutonium program, the latter was actually initiated some time before the uranium isotope separation effort.

We now know that the Soviets have mastered the difficult art of producing porous nickel membranes for the gaseous diffusion process, that there are gaseous diffusion plant facilities operating in the USSR, that they produce large quantities of U-235, and that Soviet military demands restrict the use of that material "for peaceful purposes." Thus, the Soviets now possess the weapons and power reactor design versatility provided by the availability of both uranium-235 and plutonium.

The earliest known Soviet plutonium work after the renewal of their effort, specifically directed toward achieving a nuclear chain reaction, relates to "The Theory of Resonance in Small Uranium Lumps." This was precisely the same type of theoretical work that was then being conducted at the University of Chicago, in the United States, in connection with the design of the plutonium production reactors at Hanford, Washington.

Even before the war the authors of the paper, I. I. Gurevich and I. Y. Pomeranchuk, had been engaged in similar work with Kurchatov. Their later work, which was performed in 1943 but not published until 1955, is considered by the Soviet Union to be a pioneer contribution to the theory of nuclear reactors. The fact that it was done at the same time entirely similar work was being conducted in the United States supports the following surmise: the experimental breakthrough that prompted a U.S. effort along these lines might have been the same factor that influenced the Soviet effort.

From the start Kurchatov himself had expressed a pessimistic view of the practical possibility of achieving a chain reaction and may have held this attitude until the reaction was demonstrated in the United States. In November 1940, he had stated: "I would like to stress again that although the possibility of a nuclear chain reaction has now been established in principle, tremendous practical difficulties will arise in any attempt to realize it in any of the systems which have so far been investigated."[3]

It is, then, quite conceivable that the successful chain reaction achieved at the University of Chicago on December 2, 1942, served to spur the Soviets to a renewal of their atomic energy program.

It is also probably not coincidental that in January 1943
the Soviet Purchasing Commission in the United States notified the War Production Board authorities of an intent to
request purchase of eight tons each of uranium oxide and
uranyl nitrate salts. If this amount were processed into metal
by the Soviets, it would provide just the right amount of
material necessary to duplicate the U.S. experiments at Chicago. This request for the materials was finally initiated by
the Soviet Union in April 1943, but only much smaller
amounts were granted. The first Soviet chain reaction was
not to be achieved until four years later.

At recent open atomic conferences, Soviet scientists revealed their designs of many items of atomic equipment,
including reactors. While many of their designs showed
original concepts, others clearly were adapted from Western
devices. An interesting and important example is the first
Soviet reactor to be put into operation. It was a low-power
device constructed of graphite and uranium metal. Its primary function was the testing of uranium slugs and other
material to be used in their production reactors. As such, its
function was precisely that of the so-called Hanford 305 test
reactor—the fourth nuclear reactor built in the United States.
Although this study is not a technical exposition, it will be
useful to compare some of the corresponding details of the
305 reactor with the first Soviet reactor (PSR):

	Hanford 305	PSR
Power	10 watts	10 watts
Diameter	18–20 feet	19 feet
Lattice spacing	8½ inches	8 inches
Loading	27 tons uranium	25–50 tons uranium*
Rod diameter	1.448 inches	1.2 to 1.6 inches

* Soviet estimate.

The physical comparisons noted here and the other
known characteristics of the PSR reactor are significant to

the reactor physicist; they tell him that the first Soviet reactor was practically a carbon copy of the American 305 reactor built at Hanford during the first phases of the Manhattan Project. These facts, concerning a relatively minor type of reactor, have several interesting implications:

1. By not first building a test reactor of the type that operated at the University of Chicago at the end of 1942, the Soviets showed that they were not simply interested in first demonstrating for their own benefit that a nuclear chain reaction can occur. Instead, they constructed the type of low-power reactor necessary for controlling the production of the materials of large-scale plutonium-producing reactors.

2. All data on the U.S. reactor remained secret until about 1953 (and were not completely declassified until the end of 1955); the PSR was completed many years prior to that date. The similarity of construction is interesting. Is it coincidental, or were details on the 305 reactor obtained through espionage?

3. The Soviets have not revealed the general location of their first reactor. In constructing the 305 reactor, "it was felt that certain material tests and particularly the educational programs could best be conducted right at the [production] site." The same philosophy would apply to the Soviet situation, if the reactor were to have maximum utility; however, conflicting training, uranium production, and reactor site requirements do not necessarily mean, in the Soviet case, a corresponding location for the PSR.

4. Rather than attempt an independent and improved materials testing reactor, the Soviets chose to copy a sure thing. This suggests at this stage of the Soviet program both a sense of urgency and a lack of technical self-confidence.

5. The scheduling of construction of the first Soviet reactor provides an interesting computation for the rate of progress of the Soviet atomic program.

Soviet spokesmen have not yet revealed just when the PSR went into operation, but it is possible to bracket the date in a very approximate manner by referring to oblique statements.

The Soviets, unable to boast that they had constructed the world's first nuclear reactor, console themselves with the claim that theirs was the first reactor to operate in Europe. All earlier claimants to that distinction are known, and the British Graphite Low Energy Experimental Reactor ("GLEEP"), which first operated on August 15, 1947, was previously believed to have been the first to operate outside the North American continent.*

This claim, if true, gives a "late" limit for the operation of the first Soviet reactor. Unfortunately no data are available to establish a precise "early" limit. But the peculiar nature of the claim that their reactor was "the first in Europe" rather than the naming of a specific date suggests quite strongly that the Soviets are not proud of the amount of time they required to achieve a nuclear chain reaction and that the start-up date was close to August 15, 1947. If so, the comparatively late start-up date of their first chain-reacting device must have been a source of embarrassment to Soviet scientists. Although they are now eager to establish their scientific priorities and accomplishments, they have shown an obvious reluctance to give the time schedule on their first nuclear reactor, while they have publicized the dates of later experimental reactors. For example, their first heavy water reactor was designed in 1947, installed in 1948, and put into operation in April 1949. Presumably, some operating data from the first graphite reactor would have been needed to

* The first reactor to operate outside the United States was the Canadian "ZEEP" which went into operation on September 5, 1945. Like the U.S. 305 and the Soviet PSR reactors, it operated at the low power of 10 watts, but it was of a fundamentally different type.

design the heavy water reactor, and this lends additional credence to a 1947 start-up date for the former reactor.

We can assume that it was only when these initial successes had been achieved that the Soviet atomic program began to take on important proportions. The Council of Ministers of the USSR did not give the green light to the Presidium of the Academy of Sciences on the work under the Five-Year Plan until June 1947—over a year after the Plan had started. Moreover, at the same time the Council of Ministers "considerably increased" the "allocations" for the purchase of equipment for scientific establishments. A large, serious nuclear program would place heavy budgetary demands on the over-all program of the Academy of Sciences; the sudden approval and increase of Academy of Sciences funds at this time—June 1947—appears to be another important consequence of the operation of the first Soviet reactor and the probable decision at that time to proceed with a gaseous diffusion plant for the separation of U-235.

These considerations must be coupled with the evident change in political attitudes toward the "secret" at this time. The achievement of a nuclear chain reaction is the most probable technical development that could have influenced the change from Stalin's free acknowledgment in the fall of 1946 that the Soviet Union did not yet possess the "secret" to Molotov's November 1947 boast that the "secret of the atom bomb . . . has long ago ceased to exist."

This technical development also undoubtedly influenced the gradual strengthening of the Soviet opposition to the Baruch Plan in the United Nations, which culminated in what the State Department has termed the "first positive plan" to block the majority of Western proposals.

The Soviet proposal, which in every sense was a major one, was put forward on June 11, 1947, and did not refer at all to the monopoly position of the United States, although that theme had been constantly played before that time. As recently as May 19, 1947, Andrei Gromyko had implicitly admitted the "monopoly" of the United States but strongly hinted that it was on the verge of collapse:

But it is beyond any doubt that the position of monopoly for one country in this field is of a temporary character . . . it is impossible to stop the advance of science, not only in the United States, but in other countries as well. This relates above all to those nations which possess not only the appropriate scientific personnel but also the technical and other means necessary for carrying on work in the field of the production of atomic energy.[4]

Did this forced reference to the means for the production of atomic energy refer to their first nuclear reactor? Probably so.

Certainly, the operation of this first Soviet reactor must have given a great boost to the confidence of scientists and their leaders in the Soviet Union. This technical achievement was reflected in the new line that took effect in the summer of 1947 but that definitely was not a part of Soviet atomic policy in late 1946. Analysis of all available technical data and examination of the change in attitude toward the "secret" indicate that the first Soviet reactor went into operation about the spring of 1947—give or take a few months.

Other details of the scheduling of the PSR vis-à-vis the 305 provide additional significant data on the Soviet project.

Design having started in June 1943, the 305 reactor was completed in March 1944, went into operation in April, and was first used for testing uranium slugs for production reactors in May 1944, or about three years before the first Soviet reactor began operating. If the Soviet design and construction were on a similar schedule, design on it would have been started in June 1946—or about a full year after an atomic bomb burst over Hiroshima.

Considering the fact that the Soviets apparently had data

on the construction of the U.S. 305 reactor and that they had done independent theoretical work on reactors of this type, the very significant delay in constructing this most simple of reactor types must have been occasioned by one or both of the following considerations:

1. The Soviets may have been extremely cautious (or argumentative) in their approach to atomic energy and simply required a year of postwar thought to decide on the method and the course to take. For example, there was the important decision on whether plutonium or uranium-235 bombs should be made—or whether it was necessary to embark on both types of programs. The nature of the first Soviet reactor is in itself evidence of serious intent to at least embark on building up a plutonium production capacity.

It should be noted that the first postwar Five-Year Plan did not get under way until the spring of 1946; simple bureaucratic necessity may have dictated this scheduling on the full-scale postwar atomic program. A matter of probable bearing on these decisions is that it was not until June 1946 that General Boris Lvovich Vannikov, administrative director of the Soviet atomic energy program in this postwar period, was relieved of his additional duties as Minister of Agricultural Machine Building (the postwar cover name for the Soviet munitions industry). Henceforth, the Soviet atomic energy program was conducted under the cover of the First Chief Department (Directorate) of the Council of Ministers on a priority basis.

The Dean of the Physics Faculty of Moscow State University, who was involved in the construction of the first Soviet reactor, has openly admitted that he and his colleagues were not at all confident of the success of their effort. Regarding the preliminary work for the reactor, he stated:

. . . the measurements themselves, as well as the calculations in which the results of measurements were utilized, were not very accurate at that time. That is why we had no absolute confidence at that time in the ultimate success of our attempt to realize the chain reaction in a system built up of natural uranium and graphite.[5]

Apparently, Soviet nuclear scientists were impressed and even awed by the magnificent nuclear production complexes that had been built in the United States.

Lev Landau, the outstanding nuclear theoretician, wrote just after the Hiroshima and Nagasaki bomb drops—and before the war had ended—"The solution of these complex problems in a four-year period is an enormous scientific technical achievement, of which the physicists and engineers of countries allied to ours might rightfully be proud."[6]

Stalin's scientists may have convinced even him of the enormity of the Anglo-American undertaking. At a dinner at Moscow on Christmas Eve, 1945, Stalin told the U.S. Secretary of State, James F. Byrnes, that "although scientists spoke a language he did not clearly understand, they did a wonderful work and he thought those American scientists responsible for the discovery of atomic energy were to be especially congratulated."[7] A few moments later Stalin rebuffed a disparaging remark that Molotov had made to James B. Conant, a key figure in the Manhattan Project: "Generalissimo Stalin . . . arose and said he was not satisfied to dismiss Dr. Conant's work thus lightly. He believed, he said, that Dr. Conant and his associates had rendered a great service and he wanted to congratulate them upon their success."

These remarks of Stalin's at the end of 1945 indicate that his scientists had not made any rash promises to him on their ability to achieve a nuclear chain reaction—the first important step on the way to production of an atomic bomb. It was a cautious and safe attitude to adopt.

2. The materials of construction of such a reactor as the PSR, mainly graphite and metallic uranium, may simply not

THEIR FIRST CHAIN REACTION

have been available in sufficient quantity or purity to permit an earlier scheduling. Here again, the production of these items may have been tied in with the postwar Five-Year Plan.

No matter how many data may have been available through published or espionage channels, or how much theoretical and experimental design had been performed by competent Soviet physicists, the real test was whether Soviet industry could furnish the graphite and metallic uranium in required bulk and purity. Evidently, Soviet scientists were apprehensive about the purity aspect from the start. The same Soviet scientist mentioned above, V. S. Fursov, has confessed:

It should also be added that the purity of such large quantities of graphite and uranium as were required for building the reactor had to be no lower than the purity of the samples studied in our previous experiments. In any event, there was some reason to consider the proposed construction of the uranium-graphite reactor as something other than a completely guaranteed undertaking.[8]

It apparently took a while for Soviet industry to supply the materials, but "after it became possible to secure the quantity of material specified . . . we began to build the reactor."

Even at the final construction stage of the first Soviet reactor, the purity problem must have been worrisome—for the reactor had to be loaded with far more than the estimated minimum amount of uranium before the chain reaction began to occur. The very similar U.S. reactor took only 27 tons of uranium, while the Soviet reactor would not operate on less than 45 tons, which was close to the most pessimistic Soviet estimates. Moreover, this amount of uranium metal seems to have been all that was available in the Soviet Union at that time, for they had to employ all the uranium slugs left over from their preliminary experiments as well as to utilize a small number of briquettes of nonmetallic uranium compounds on the periphery of the active zone of the reactor.

Thus, in an apparent frenzy to complete their first nuclear chain reaction, Soviet scientists utilized every last bit of uranium at their disposal. But success was achieved. The operation of their first chain-reacting device must have been a source of accomplishment and relief to Soviet scientists. With added confidence, they were now in a position to make some of the promises that Stalin must have expected of them.

10

THE BOMB

Although two and one-half years were required from the time the Russians completed their first nuclear reactor to the explosion of the atomic weapon that was announced by President Truman on September 23, 1949, the Soviets officially chose to date their possession of the atomic bomb from November 1947, which was the date by which they felt that they could proceed confidently. In confirming President Truman's announcement of two days earlier, TASS stated on September 25, 1949:

As for the production of atomic energy, TASS considers it necessary to recall that already on November 6, 1947, Minister of Foreign Affairs of the USSR V. M. Molotov made a statement concerning the secret of the atom bomb, when he declared that this secret was already long non-existent.

This statement signified the Soviet Union already had discovered the secret of the atomic weapon and that it had at its disposal this weapon.

Scientific circles of the United States of America took this statement of V. M. Molotov for bluff, considering that the Russians could not possess an atomic weapon earlier than the year 1952.

They, however, were mistaken, since the Soviet Union possessed the secret of the atomic weapon already in 1947.[1]

This claim is illustrative of the retrospective and quantitative projections that have been characteristic of many of the Soviet claims to arms superiority. Soviet disclosure philosophy seems to consider that once a certain qualitative stage is reached—that is, when it is known how to proceed and a weapon is effectively under production—then this automatically implies possession of the weapon. Consistent with this philosophy, an announcement of a weapon capability also usually falsely implies that the Soviet stockpile of that weapon is boundless, or at least sufficient. It is peculiar how Western reaction bolsters the operation of such a crude propaganda device. For it seems that some Western observers may be prone to express skepticism of a particular Soviet development, but, once it has been developed, the same observers automatically assume the validity of anything else rumored or stated about the weapon.

Regarding the atomic explosion that occurred on August 29, 1949, it is interesting to observe the interval of two years and several months that occurred from the time of the operation of the first Soviet reactor and compare it with the two-and-one-half-year interval between the operation of the first nuclear reactor at Chicago on December 2, 1942, and the detonation of the first atomic bomb on July 16, 1945. Perhaps the proper inference is that the Soviet development rate was approximately the same as that of the United States in the early stages of its atomic program. However, it has been shown that the first Soviet reactor more nearly corresponded to the Hanford test reactor that came into operation in the United States in April 1944. On a strictly comparative basis,

the Soviet Union should have tested its first bomb in the fall
of 1948! It is therefore possible that the early Soviet program
was retarded and experienced difficulties of an unknown
nature between the spring of 1947 and the fall of 1949. This
delay, coupled with a similar one in bringing their first test
reactor into operation, indicates that up to 1949, at least, the
Soviet developmental rate was slower than that of the United
States, but not as slow as many prognostications at that time
suggested.

There is, of course, an alternate explanation to consider: namely, the possibility that the bomb announced by
President Truman was not the first atomic bomb detonated
in the USSR. The U.S. foreign test detection system was
initiated only "in sufficient time to detect a Soviet nuclear
explosion which occurred on the 29th of August, 1949."[2]
The initial Soviet reaction to the President's announcement
was quite flustered, and for a number of days they were completely unprepared to exploit their achievement sensibly.
It is quite conceivable that if a bomb or bombs had been
detonated earlier, and they had not been detected by the
United States, then they would not have been announced
by the Soviet Union. In the absence of other information,
however, the 1949 detonation must be regarded, at least, as
the first successful Soviet nuclear explosion.

Indeed, most of the statements about the Soviet test program have come from the U.S. Atomic Energy Commission.
A few of the AEC announcements have been confirmed, but
the Soviet Union evidently prefers to remain silent on the
majority of them. It is essentially from the official statements
of the AEC that we must infer the probable nature of Soviet
nuclear weapons development to date, for no other information is available. The policy of the AEC is not to announce
every Soviet atomic test; sometimes the AEC announcements
indicate only that a series of tests has been held. By the spring
of 1958 the AEC had announced 39 Soviet tests or series of

tests. Only a handful of Soviet test announcements had originated from Soviet official sources. No Soviet test series, as
such, has ever been announced in advance of its occurrence.
The total number of Soviet atomic tests is well in excess of
50, and can be compared with the total (to April 1958) of
well over 100 tests conducted by the United States. However,
these sums are not especially meaningful in making a comparison of the nuclear position of the USSR vis-à-vis the
United States.

A period of two years passed before another Soviet test
was held. Stalin confirmed the October 1951 test and commented that "tests of atomic bombs of different calibers will
be conducted in the future as well." The U.S. Operation
Ranger, which consisted of five tests and was directed toward
the development of tactical weapons, had been conducted
earlier that year in Nevada, and a number of tests relating
to thermonuclear development had been conducted in April
and May at Eniwetok. The announcement of a Soviet test
on October 22, 1951, corresponded with the start of a new
U.S. test series in Nevada. Another two years passed without
any Soviet tests. Then, on August 8, 1953, Malenkov boasted
before the Supreme Soviet: "The USA has long since lost
the monopoly in the matter of the production of atomic
bombs. . . . The government deems it necessary to report
to the Supreme Soviet that the U.S. has no monopoly in the
production of the hydrogen bomb either."[3] This announcement was met with considerable skepticism in the West until
four days later when the Soviets detonated a nuclear device
that involved both fission and thermonuclear reactions.
TASS confirmed the U.S. announcement with the following
statement:

One of a variety of hydrogen bombs was exploded for experimental purposes in the Soviet Union within the past few
days. Because a powerful thermonuclear reaction was created

in the hydrogen bomb, the explosion was of great strength. The tests showed that the power of the hydrogen bomb is many times greater than the power of the atom bomb. It is known that the Soviet Union has had the atomic weapon for several years and has conducted suitable tests.[4]

Malenkov took no risk in making his announcement previous to the test, for indeed all that he claimed was that the hydrogen bomb was in production in the Soviet Union, and this was true. Had the bomb not succeeded in the August test, it would not have been detected as a hydrogen bomb, the TASS announcement would not have claimed it as such, and the world would simply have waited with uncertainty for a Russian thermonuclear test.

Actually it is probable that their first hydrogen device was an exceedingly cumbersome affair—not a bomb. As the TASS announcement indicated, it was an experimental device, and a publication of the U.S. Joint Committee on Atomic Energy states that the device was "nondeliverable." The 1954 Soviet series was not confirmed by the Russians. Beginning in August 1955, an extensive series was started, culminating in the test of a deliverable hydrogen bomb dropped from an aircraft on November 23, 1955. At that time Khrushchev was visiting in India, and on September 26 in his Bangalore speech, he said:

An announcement has been published today in the papers of many countries, including some Indian papers, that an atomic explosion has been set off in the Soviet Union. I shall not say that there has not been such an explosion. It was a terrific explosion. Tomorrow our press will publish an announcement to this effect.

Recently, in compliance with the plan for research and experimental work in atomic energy, new types of atomic and thermonuclear weapons have been tested in our country. These tests have confirmed completely the corresponding scientific calculations. They have also demonstrated the important new achievements of Soviet scientists and engineers.

The latest experimental explosion of an "H"-bomb has been the most powerful yet staged. Using a relatively small quantity of fissionable material, our scientists and engineers have managed to produce an explosion equal to that of several megatons of conventional explosives.[5]

The next day's TASS announcement repeated much of what Khrushchev had said and noted in addition that "the explosion was set off at a high altitude in order to prevent radioactive effects." In a speech before the Supreme Soviet on December 29, 1955, Khrushchev recalled the November test and declared that "its power of many millions of tons of explosives could be substantially increased."

Khrushchev's reference at Bangalore to a reduction in the amount of fissionable material required to produce a multimegaton explosion is not very different from the more widely publicized information that he gave in an interview with Senator Hubert H. Humphrey on December 1, 1958. In the latter conversation, Khrushchev referred specifically to a "five-million-ton bomb" requiring less than a tenth of the amount of fissionable material that would previously have been necessary. If Khrushchev meant a *further* reduction in fissionable material beyond that mentioned in 1955, his later statement could have had some significance, but its exact relationship to the earlier claim could not be properly assessed on the basis of Khrushchev's statement alone. In either event, it should be recognized that the technique of thermonuclear bomb design is complex and may go in several directions. Vague reference to the amounts of fissionable material involved is not in itself meaningful, for a thermonuclear bomb, by definition, is one that requires a reduced amount of fissionable material.

An extensive Soviet test series was conducted in 1956. Many of these tests were to perfect atomic warheads for tactical purposes. Until 1956, according to a White House statement, approximately 80 per cent of the U.S. tests had been of fission devices and the remainder thermonuclear. Examination of the meager data available indicates approximately the same ratio for the Soviets.

Available data do not permit a comparison of the U.S. and Soviet thermonuclear technologies or a description of whether or not the U.S. claims represented a more sophisticated or advanced approach. Although the United States tested two types of hydrogen bombs in November 1952 and March 1954, the first U.S. H-bomb to be tested in an actual drop from an aircraft was detonated on May 21, 1956. It should be noted that in both the U.S. and USSR programs there was considerable lag between the achievement of nondeliverable and deliverable devices.

At a 1954 presidential press conference the Chairman of the AEC confirmed the initial Soviet lead. Mr. Strauss stated:

In August of last year the Russians also tested a weapon or device of a yield well beyond the range of regular fission weapons and which derived a part of its force from the fusion of light elements. There is good reason to believe that they had begun work on this weapon substantially before we did.[6]

Retrospectively, it must be seen that President Truman's decision in January 1950 to proceed with the construction of the H-bomb did not initiate an "H-bomb race." That contest had already begun.

Evidently, the Soviets chose to rely on the impression ingrained by the November 1955 test, for, except for the announcement of some tests in the autumn of 1956, the Soviets have confirmed few of the numerous later announcements of the AEC. Some of these tests were to perfect "new types of weapons for various arms of the services." The Soviet test program had been conducted at a continuously accelerating rate to the extent that in early 1958 there were a number of instances of two tests being conducted on the same day. Where this was so, one of the tests was usually conducted at an internal site such as the Central Asian proving ground (near Semipalatinsk, about 300 miles west of the Chinese-Mongolian border), and the other at the test site above the Arctic Circle at a location on the Barents Sea (in the vicinity of Novaya Zemlya Island). Generally, the larger tests (in the megaton range) have been conducted at the northern site, with the lower yield detonations occurring at the internal test ranges.

The emphasis on minimizing radioactive fall-out in the Soviet test announcements and the physical fact that fall-out from the southern site could likely occur on nearby communities indicate the possibility that the Soviet test program had been hampered by fall-out considerations until the northern site was available. It is not known whether or not Russian cities have ever experienced serious fall-out, but following the April 1956 detonations the Peking radio warned of high levels of fall-out in the area. Madame Le Teh Chuan, the Minister of Public Health, urged the public to wash food in boiling water before consuming it. It is extraordinary that the announcements specifically identified the fall-out as originating from the Soviet Siberian test site.

The Peking situation was probably not unique. The Central Asian test site lies approximately at the 50th parallel; the shots occurring at that location have been particularly "dirty" in regard to fall-out. In fact, the peak in latitudinal fall-out has occurred in a band around the earth roughly at the 45th parallel north, and a great fraction of the long-lived fission products deposited in that band is due to the Russian test program.

Although, on a yield basis, the Soviet total of about 50 megatons corresponds to somewhat less than half of the total detonated by the United States and Britain, the conditions of burst and types of bomb used in Soviet tests have contributed a highly disproportionate amount of world-wide fall-out.

The accelerated test schedule in 1958 was probably coupled with the intense Soviet drive for the abolition of nuclear tests. Three megaton-range weapons were exploded within a period of five days, and six more nuclear weapons within a period of nine days. By the fall of 1958 the Soviets had a broad family of nuclear weapons. Although we could infer from the relative number of tests that the number of types of nuclear bombs incorporated in the Soviet stockpile is not as extensive as that in the U.S. stockpile, the entirely different strategic position of the USSR and the methods of accomplishing its ultimate aims differ quite sharply from Western defense philosophy. It is not reasonable to expect an identical atomic weapon program or an identical philosophy of use. Perhaps the most significant inference arises from the fact that the Soviet tests have, for the most part, been particularly "dirty"; that is, there appears to be relatively less emphasis on "clean" nuclear weapons.

Until Stalin's death there was an insufficient realization of basic nuclear facts among Soviet military planners for effective political exploitation and military preparation in atomic warfare. Starting on January 14, 1954, a series of articles in *Red Star,* an official military organ, heralded the general release of atomic information to all levels of the military. Four years later the nuclear facts of life were sufficiently ingrained in the Soviet political and military leaders to embolden them to display various degrees of flexibility in their nuclear weapons policy.

The Soviets have realized that perhaps the most important use of their atomic stockpile, whatever may be its composition, is as a political weapon. History may show that inert nuclear weapons, adroitly handled in a political sense, have produced changes dissimilar to all-out global conflict, but just as profound.

In a speech to his Kalinin constituents on March 14, 1958, Khrushchev made the following points:

> The past four years have been years in which the Soviet Union, together with other peace-loving nations, has persistently tried to relax international tension, to stop the armaments race, and to avert a new war. The most burning and vital problem for all mankind at present is the problem of peace and war. Wars between states always bring many victims and vast destruction. But a future war, should it break out in spite of the will of the peoples, threatens to be the most destructive of all—a nuclear war. Apart from the direct damage, the use of nuclear arms will poison the atmosphere by radioactive fall-out and this may lead to the destruction of nearly all living organisms, especially in countries with restricted territory and dense population. Everything there can quite literally be wiped off the face of the earth.
>
> The level of armaments in certain countries has reached such a stage that the time will come, and perhaps it has come already, when these countries themselves, irrespective of whether or not an agreement on the cessation of production of atomic and hydrogen arms has been reached, will have to say "enough." If formerly old arms and military techniques were replaced as new models were created, now it appears that a stage has been reached when it is difficult to invent more powerful arms than the hydrogen weapon, the power of which is limitless. It is no accident that scientists, though as yet shyly, declare that if the stocks of nuclear arms which have been stored were exploded, the atmosphere of the entire terrestrial globe may be poisoned.[7]

Thus Khrushchev hinted that the Soviet Union might unilaterally decide to suspend tests and the production of nuclear arms. A "decision" to suspend testing was announced by Gromyko before the Supreme Soviet on March 31, 1958. The obvious advantage of a unilaterally declared suspension is that it places no obligation on the declarer to accept internal inspection. Moreover, the conditional phrasing of Gromyko's declaration, that the Soviet government would consider itself free to resume its tests if other powers continued theirs, provided adequate insurance for this powerful propaganda play. Resume the tests they did, in the fall of 1958, at their Novaya Zemlya test locale just before serious test suspension talks were to begin. Indeed, even during the initial conference days, more weapons were tested at an internal USSR site. And on February 3, 1959, Igor Kurchatov boasted of the latter tests before the Twenty-first Party Congress:

It should be said here that these tests proved to be most successful. They have shown the great effectiveness of certain new principles worked out by Soviet scientists and engineers. As a result, the Soviet Army received still more powerful, more perfect, reliable, compact, and cheaper atomic and hydrogen weapons.[8]

Coming from Kurchatov, here is a meaningful, comprehensive claim. It is probable that the types of atomic weapons now in the Soviet stockpile may be deemed sufficient for any foreseeable military operation during the trial period of a test suspension. In addition, the USSR stockpile may be coupled with delivery systems that give a high degree of expected effectiveness.

It should be noted, moreover, that the Soviets in their 1955 statements were proud to mention that their tests confirmed the calculations previously carried out. Then, of course, there is inherent in Malenkov's August 8, 1953, speech a confidence that their first H-bomb test would work. The Soviet leaders may feel that if it does become necessary to refabricate their atomic stockpile into more advanced types, as demanded, their scientists' calculation techniques are sufficiently reliable to guarantee operable weapons without tests. Also, the U.S. long-range monitoring program is able to detect certain characteristics of Soviet weapons by comparison with data collected in U.S. tests. It follows that a reciprocal relationship must be valid to some extent, and that it may be unnecessary for the USSR to test certain bomb-design parameters because they have already been tested by the United States. But the military commander will always feel that there is some risk in employing untested weapons; regardless of political and relative military gains that may arise by proposing test cessation, there will always be strong internal pressures in the USSR to continue testing.

Soviet political and military planners undoubtedly realize that increasing the number of bombs may offset certain disadvantages of design curtailment. The production of power from atomic energy is essentially a peaceful pursuit, but a usual by-product of nuclear reactors producing electricity is the creation of additional fissionable material, namely, plutonium or uranium-233. The Russian industrial atomic power program is expanding at an exceedingly high rate, which means that the production of fissionable material in their atomic power reactors will soon match and exceed that of the military reactors. In fact, their largest "peaceful" atomic power station produces electricity inefficiently, apparently for the purpose of optimizing plutonium production. Having created a peaceful program on the basis of a military atomic energy program, the former will soon be able to give significant support to the latter.

Much of what the Soviets do militarily, economically, and in their political offensive will depend on the atomic energy structure that has been created, their peaceful atomic energy program, their natural resources, and the unknown advances that further research may bring. And for quite some time Soviet scientists have spoken of certain applications of atomic energy that are only now beginning to be appreciated in the West.

11

THE GENERAL'S PLOWSHARES

In a poem published in July 1949 by Stalin prize winner Yevgenii Aronovich Dolmatovskii, a father comforts his baby daughter, who has just been disturbed by "the distant hollow rumble" from the Taiga far away. He whispers:

You shuddered. The distant hollow rumble
Of your carriage
Sounded like a wind.
Sleep, my baby,
Your doll, your teddy bear and your little black devil
    are sleeping peacefully like children.
Where did that sudden jolt come from?
What does that signify?
In the Taiga, far away from here
In quite another end of the country,
Where the color of the yellow leaves
Does not glow away until spring.

There stands a granite mountain
Which is barring our way.
Long, long ago it should have been turned

Upside down,
Long, long ago it should have been forced to give up
    its ore.
Sleep, my daughter,
The night is dark,
Sleep, my baby.
At that place there lived a group of geologists
In frost and heat.
Twelve months long
They were crawling around on the mountain.

Then there came an airplane full of professors to that
    place and then a platoon of army engineers,
First-class lads,
And their young commander,
And he was ordered to lay down an explosive shell.
It was not gunpowder, nor dynamite.
There is far more powerful stuff
Now in your country.
I shall not tell its name.
Sleep, my baby.

At the prearranged hour, the explosion occurred.
The granite was blown asunder to dust.
The Taiga around the mountain was illuminated
By golden radiance.
The ancient mountain disappeared and the roar of the
    explosion interrupted at five in the morning
The sleep of children
As a breath of wind
From far, far away.

Sleep, little girl,
Your hand lies in my hand.
May the sound wave reach the foreign coasts
And warn our enemies
Who hear it there.
The mountain wasted away like flame and gave away
    its ore,
Not long ago only a fairy tale,
This has now occurred.
Sleep, my baby.[1]

On March 6, 1958, the U.S. AEC announced that it is engaged in a "Project Plowshare," the purpose of which is to investigate the possible applications of nuclear explosions for peaceful purposes; and as one of the applications, it is suggested that nuclear explosions could crush large masses of rock and thus be used to break up ore bodies for removal. Did Soviet scientists anticipate these applications a decade earlier? Dolmatovskii's poem would suggest so. For several years the bomb itself was the major tool of Soviet "peaceful atom" propaganda.

The sound waves from Dolmatovskii's new explosive evidently did not reach the foreign coasts as quickly as intended. Unless Western nuclear-detection systems had failed or had not been fully developed yet, the poem would seem to have been published prematurely. The official TASS announcement that appeared two months later, on September 25, 1949, coyly and indirectly recognized U.S. detection of the first Soviet A-bomb in the following words:

As is known, construction work is being conducted on a large scale in the Soviet Union—the construction of hydroelectric stations, mines, canals, and roads, which necessarily call for much blasting, using the latest technical methods. As this blasting has taken place and is taking place rather frequently in various regions of the country, it is possible that this could attract attention beyond the borders of the Soviet Union.[2]

Again, there is reference, through the use of the words "latest technical methods," to the application of nuclear explosions for peaceful purposes. The TASS applications were again unconsciously echoed in the AEC's March 6, 1958, release wherein it was stated that an application of nuclear explosions would be "moving earth in quantity such as digging a large canal."

The TASS announcement was exuberantly exploited by the late Andrei Vishinsky in the United Nations (on No-

vember 10, 1949) to the extent of his claiming that atomic
energy was being used in the Soviet Union for "razing mountains, . . . irrigating deserts, . . . cutting through jungle
and tundra." Russia's changing political aims dictated that
no nuclear detonation should be recognized as having a
benign application, and the Chief Soviet Delegate at the
1958 Geneva Conference on the Peaceful Uses of Atomic
Energy confessed to a cloistered existence the greater part of
his life: "I do not remember what Vishinsky said, because
I never used to listen to politicians, although I now do."

Because of the growing technical and political importance
of peaceful atomic applications, it is important to examine
whether or not the USSR had indeed seriously considered
such applications despite Comrade Yemel'yanov's assertions,
and whether it has some incentive to utilize atomic explosions for peaceful purposes. The outstanding and virtually
the only public spokesman for such applications in the
Soviet Union has been Doctor of Technical Sciences, Professor Georgii Iosifovich Pokrovskii, Major General of Engineering Services. General Pokrovskii has the distinction of
being the most prolific spokesman on almost every technical
matter, with major emphasis on atomic energy and space
travel, in the Soviet popular and technical press. A professor
at the Zhukovskii Military-Aviation Engineering Institute,
Pokrovskii is a man of some technical ability, having originally been a nuclear physicist who in the 1930's switched to
problems of soil mechanics. During the war he worked on
problems of conventional explosives and the development of
shaped charges; so his general background should make him
an expert on the moving of earth by means of nuclear explosions.

Writing mainly in such popular journals as *Ogonek*
(*Little Flame*) and *Tekhnika Molodezhi* (*Technology for
Youth*), General Pokrovskii has consistently advocated the

application of large-scale explosives for large earth-moving projects, and he has noted that the size of the explosions required in such projects would be approximately the same as the yield of atomic bombs.

Large-scale detonations of conventional explosives have been carried out behind the Iron Curtain. Some of them are comparable to, or larger than, any equivalent operation conducted in the West. In order to tap an ore body near the northern Chinese city of Lanchow, the Soviet technical group that specializes in large-scale explosions, Soiuzvzryv-prom, set off in the last half of 1956 several immense explosions: on July 19 a charge of 1,640 tons was exploded; on November 15 a charge of 4,000 tons; and on December 31 a charge of 9,200 tons. Pokrovskii has also stated that until 1956 no conventional explosive charge exceeding 2,500 tons had ever been set off. Evidently, even this charge, which Pokrovskii belittles, must have been set off by the Soviets, for the largest nonatomic explosions ever detonated in the West, to 1958, have not exceeded 1,500 tons. The largest Western nonatomic charge, involving 1,375 tons of explosives, was detonated on April 5, 1958, to destroy a channel hazard in the Alaskan waterway. What is most striking, however, is that the majority of large-scale explosions have occurred in China. These continued through the period when experts in Geneva were meeting to decide on the feasibility of distinguishing such explosions from nuclear tests. For example, on January 13, 1959, Soviet experts supervised a large-scale "directed" explosion at the site of the Tung-chwankow reservoir.

At a Utah construction project where engineers blasted loose a cliffside to obtain dirt for a railroad causeway over an adjoining lake, the total amount of explosives set off was a mere 1,065 tons. Pokrovskii had stated that a project, which seems quite similar to the Utah project, would be undertaken for a railroad running from Paoki to Chengtu in Central China.

The AEC has suggested that Project Plowshare could be used for "piping water into a rock formation heated by a contained nuclear detonation to form steam for producing power or for other purposes." This application and others of a more imaginative nature have also been anticipated by General Pokrovskii.

Toward the end of 1957, apparently only for the purpose of obtaining more detailed experimental data, a 1,000-ton charge was exploded at Tagansai, seventy miles north of Tashkent, in Uzbekistan. The experiment was conducted with a great deal of auxiliary apparatus to measure explosive effects. The "complex expedition" conducting the operation was composed of members of many institutes, including representatives of the Institute of Chemical Physics, the Institute of Earth Physics, and Moscow State University. Led by the Vice President of the Academy of Sciences, M. A. Lavrentiev (who is also Director of the new Siberian Hydrodynamics Institute), the expedition evidently had extraordinary status. Because of its special nature, it is possible that the Tagansai explosion was an attempt to emulate the U.S. underground nuclear shot Rainier, which occurred on September 19, 1957 (with a TNT strength of 1,700 tons).

It was stated that the information obtained from the Tagansai explosion would be helpful in solving an important problem that exists with respect to a gigantic new power station being built in Siberia on the Angara River, above Irkutsk. The Bratsk hydroelectric station, which will dam up the Angara River, will have a capacity of 4,500 megawatts, which will make it one of the largest hydroelectric stations in the world. The construction of the Bratsk station is almost completed, but the difficulty is that at the rate at which the Angara's waters flow northward from Lake Baikal, it will take eight to ten years to fill the Bratsk reservoir. The Russians contemplate increasing this flow by widening the bed of the Angara by a single 30,000-ton charge to be placed under the river bed. A 30,000-ton charge is one and one-half times the size of one of the first U.S. nominal atomic bombs. It is therefore an impressive explosion. If 30,000 tons of conventional explosive were placed in a single chamber, the cavity would have to be of huge dimensions (of the order of one million cubic feet), and it is probably out of the question to build such a chamber under a river bed. Moreover, it would be difficult to detonate simultaneously all parts of such a massive explosive. One can only conclude that if an atomic bomb has not been considered for this application as an obvious and convenient explosive instrument, the Soviets may be missing a good bet.

In connection with their explosives construction program, Soviet seismologists have conducted extensive physical investigations relating to the detection of distant nuclear detonations. If a test is conducted such that no radioactive products are vented to the atmosphere, major interest then centers on seismic detection.

The official Soviet position was expressed by Gromyko on May 10, 1957: "It is usually said that it is possible to test atomic and hydrogen bombs without the explosions being detected. This is at variance with the facts."[3]

Coordinated by the Central Seismic Station at Moscow, data from a network of 70 seismic stations are continuously analyzed. After boasting of the detection of the U.S. bomb tests, the Soviet seismologists had said as early as September 1956:

It should be pointed out that the instruments of such seismographic stations register all types of shocks—surface, underground, over water, and under water. Thus, contemporary technical methods make it possible to detect all kinds of tests of atomic and hydrogen weapons at any point of the earth's globe.[4]

The day that Gromyko announced the conditional suspension of Soviet nuclear tests, the leading personality in the Soviet atomic program, Igor Kurchatov, made a very strong statement regarding detection:

It is sometimes said that it is impossible to check whether one state or another is carrying out tests of atomic and hydrogen weapons. This is simply irresponsible talk. It is well known that many methods exist with the aid of which explosions of atomic and hydrogen bombs can be detected at long-range distances. This includes, for instance, the study of seismic oscillations, subsonic waves, and radioactivity of the atmosphere.

The Supreme Soviet should know that we also have at our disposal other even more sensitive means of detecting distant explosions of atomic and hydrogen bombs.[5]

Some of these means, which involve acoustic, radio, and other physical phenomena, were discussed at the 1958–59 Geneva conferences on nuclear test suspension. And while the Western scientists were unable to acquiesce to Soviet claims approaching 100 per cent detectability, tentative agreement was reached on detection networks and systems that would indicate high probabilities (but not absolute certainty) of detection of nuclear tests carried out under various conditions.

In an inspection arrangement on the monitoring of nuclear tests, it would be extremely important that attention be given to the status of explosion-construction programs. Many of the detonations of conventional explosives that the Soviets have achieved and will employ are of the same size as the detonation of a small atomic bomb. Such explosions will probably be undistinguishable, as far as seismographic detection is concerned, from explosions of small nuclear bombs and vice versa. Would the Soviets allow inspection of all such explosions by international teams to confirm their nuclear or nonnuclear origin? Or would they claim all or most of such detonations to be of nonnuclear origin, involving construction projects that are the internal concern of only the USSR, and therefore not subject to inspection? This would be an especially serious point if a quota agreement on inspection were established. For if construction-type explosions are to become more frequent (which certainly seems to be the case), they could easily exhaust the set quotas.

Then there is the question of how China enters into the picture. China is not a member of the United Nations, and it is difficult to see how, under these circumstances, she would fit into the inspection system. Designed without regard to politically inaccessible voids, the detection system proposed by the East-West experts in the summer of 1958 would be seriously weakened if a large area of the world were closed to instruments and inspection. A precedent is already established for conducting very large explosions in China. The Soviets (and later the Chinese) could continue to do so, using and testing nuclear devices with an immunity guaranteed by the vast geographical and political void of Red China.

12

"OUR ATOM OF PEACE"

The Soviets may have made their first bid in the race toward industrial use of the atom as early as the fall of 1949, when serious work began on the small power demonstration reactor that came into operation four and one-half years later on June 27, 1954. The Russians boast that this was an unusually short development time. Perhaps it was, considering the fact that during most of that period, governments were not overly enthusiastic about the use of atomic energy for power.

In a society where art must reflect the accomplishments of the people, a poem was written by Igor Vol'skii to commemorate this achievement:

ATOMS FOR PEACE

Read,
        drink with your eyes the lines:
The inevitable came true, the newest of
        the miracles of the earth—

The uranium forces
    by electric current
Over Soviet wires started to run!
And somewhere,
    echoing to hearts inspired,
In this festive—humdrum hour,
In honor of peace
    new motors began to drone,
And flashed up
    the lamps of Il'ich.
The river of Time
    will carry away into silence
The cannibal's pyre
    on the island Eniwetok,*
But our Atom of Peace—
    child of Five-Year Plans,
For people
    will shine for ages,
What was a dream, a fledgling yesterday,
Today is trying out
    its powerful wings.
Glory be to those masters,
Who, out of the fairy tales
    of the days bygone,
Created this reality.[1]

The poem reflects a major purpose of this station, which is to divert attention from the military nuclear program of the USSR. In implementing the propaganda, many foreign delegations have been allowed to visit the station during the five years of its operation. These delegations have included such eminent people as the Prime Minister of India and the heads of various satellite states, as well as scientists and statesmen from Western countries. The station forms the nucleus

* *Trud*'s footnote: "The Island Eniwetok in the Pacific Ocean is a proving ground for American atomic bombs where the tests brought about many sacrifices."

of the new town and scientific center of Obninsk, which is located 75 miles southwest of Moscow near Maloyaroslavets.

Regardless of its political functions, the Soviet scientists must be credited with putting into operation the first atomic power plant of any appreciable size that has delivered electrical current to a community. Many well-known scientists, including Igor Kurchatov, A. P. Aleksandrov, and A. I. Alikhanov, gave important counsel during the construction of the reactor. However, the major credit for the development of the station is given to four men, D. I. Blokhintsev, N. A. Dollezhal', A. K. Krasin, and V. A. Malikh, who received Lenin prizes in 1957 for their accomplishment.

The electrical output of the station is small—approximately 5,000 kilowatts—and is derived from a reactor (abbreviated GVF) operating at a thermal rating of 30,000 kilowatts, using a graphite moderator and a coolant of water under pressure of 100 atmospheres, which circulates through the reactor core and gives up its heat through a system of heat exchangers to water in a second circuit. The fuel is uranium enriched to approximately 5 per cent in the U-235 component. The fact that the station has operated continuously and successfully for over five years is a matter of great satisfaction to the scientists at Obninsk.

The station has also contributed a large measure of the encouragement that Soviet planners must have needed to project, as part of the Sixth Five-Year Plan in 1956, a large atomic power program that would involve the construction of a number of atomic power stations with a total capacity of 2,000 to 2,500 megawatts of electrical output. The first of these stations was to come into operation in 1958; more were to become operative in 1959; and the rest, in 1960. There is considerable evidence that all parties concerned in the planning of these stations were not fully coordinated at the time the initial announcements were made. The statements by various scientists of the Academy of Sciences, by officials of the Chief Directorate for the Utilization of Atomic Energy (Glavatom), and by officials of the Ministry of Electric Power Stations often were in direct conflict. From the data given on the individual plants it was impossible to see how the total capacity could add up to 2,000–2,500 megawatts by 1960. Indeed, the sums corresponded to less than one-half of those amounts. Evidently, the atomic power goals were only one of the economic and industrial plans that had to be revised, for in September 1957 the Sixth Five-Year Plan was officially abandoned and most of its aims were extended in a new Seven-Year Plan that began in 1959. The atomic power targets were among those that were extended, but specific quantitative goals were not announced to the delegates of the Twenty-first Party Congress in January 1959.

Evidently one of the major reasons for the abandonment of the earlier atomic power goals was the realization that atomic power was still far from being an economic venture. As a matter of fact, when Deputy Premier Frol Kozlov visited the United States in June 1959, he confided in a private conversation that the Soviet Union was cutting back its nuclear power program because the power costs were higher than expected. He also complained that Soviet planners had been misled by their scientists on the economic aspects. Whether or not Kozlov's cutback remark means further reductions remains to be seen.*

It is still not clear how the various governmental agencies are coordinated in the atomic power program. Certainly the fuel supplies must be obtained from the Ministry of Medium Machine Building, which controls the major military and manufacturing nuclear establishments. But whether or not that Ministry is allowed to exercise any measure of technical

* *The New York Times,* July 25, 1959, p. 17.

control over the peaceful atomic power program is not known. The major engineering organization appears to be Glavatomenergo, which is a Chief Directorate of the Ministry for the Construction of Electric Power Stations, and certainly must also be subject to the strong direction of Glavatom. The Chief Engineer of Glavatomenergo is Georgii V. Yermakov.

The organization of the peaceful atomic energy program was not its only obscure aspect. The entire scheduling of which type of large atomic power station was to come into operation first—as well as the correlation of power levels, types, and location—was impossible to ascertain from the changing and conflicting public statements about the progress of the atomic power program.

Moreover, lurking in the background was the fact that the Sixth Five-Year Plan called for a "fifth station" with a 600-megawatt capacity, at an unknown "fifth location" and of an unstated type. Indeed, even this amount of information was only tenuously derived from a single speech by Igor Kurchatov before the Supreme Soviet in February 1956. Until the Second Geneva Conference on the Peaceful Utilization of Atomic Energy, which occurred in September 1958, there was no published official information to give the existence of the mysterious fifth plant any credence at all.

Professor Francis Perrin, who is head of the French atomic effort, visited the Soviet Union late in 1957, and at that time was told that a power plant with a capacity of 100 electrical megawatts would come into operation toward the end of 1958. This information received scant attention because it conflicted with current Soviet press reports that the first section of their first large atomic power plant would come into operation in 1960. However, on September 6, 1958, TASS released a communiqué consisting of just a few lines stating that a nuclear atomic power station of that capacity had indeed just been put into operation in the Soviet Union, and two days later the Chief of Glavatom, Vasilii Yemel'yanov, astounded the delegates at the Geneva Conference by showing a movie of the plant.

This plant is to be the first of six identical units comprising the station, thus giving it a total capacity of 600 electrical megawatts and a probable thermal rating of over four million kilowatts. Furthermore, the plant is at a location in Siberia that Professor Yemel'yanov declined to identify. It appears, then, that this is the fifth station of which Kurchatov spoke; aside from the surprise value of the comparatively great secrecy surrounding this plant, there must have been other compelling reasons for the abnormal silence.

The plant itself does not represent an advance in atomic power engineering; indeed, it is somewhat primitive; and if atomic power alone were the goal, it is difficult to see why five more identical units would be built. The reactor that supplies the heat is graphite moderated and fueled with natural uranium. In contrast with other nuclear power designs, the coolant is water heated only to a very low temperature, and thus the efficiency of conversion of heat to electrical energy is very low. The plant appears somewhat similar to the "dual purpose" plutonium- and electricity-producing station authorized by the U.S. 85th Congress at the Hanford plutonium plant in 1958. (Operation is scheduled for October 1962.) The primary purpose of the U.S. plant is to provide additional plutonium for weapons, with power a secondary goal. This could be the only justification for a plant of that type, since for some time to come the only use for such quantities of plutonium will be for nuclear weapons. One is then forced to conclude that the 600-megawatt Soviet station also represents a significant extension (well over one ton per year) of the Soviet Union's plutonium-producing facilities. Since it may be located at the site of one of Russia's major atomic production centers, it is easy to see why the location is being kept secret.

The propaganda value of having so large a station come into operation so soon probably exceeds the technical contribution of that particular plant to the Soviets' and the rest of the world's atomic power technology. A realistic look at this particular plant shows that its most sobering aspect should not be the atomic power technology that it represents, but the extension of the Soviet nuclear weapons stockpile. The Soviet Union can only hope to impress nuclear scientists and engineers by the other nuclear power plants it has in its program.

One of the advanced-type plants that is projected will be based on experience gained at the GVF station, which is currently being used for engineering studies for the larger station. It will be graphite-moderated and water- and steam-cooled, incorporating the feature of nuclear superheat, which represents an advanced concept in reactor technology. It was projected to have ultimately a thermal capacity of 1,150 megawatts and a gross electrical capacity of 400 megawatts, with a net electrical rating of 375 megawatts, since 25 megawatts would be expended in the operation of the station itself. In February 1956, when the designs for this large station called for an output of one-half the contemplated amount—that is, 200 megawatts—it appeared that it was to be coupled with the GVF station at Obninsk. However, this plant is presently being constructed near the village of Beloyarskoye in the Urals. Beloyarskoye is located 56 kilometers east of Sverdlovsk, and its only previous claim to fame or notoriety has been as a czarist prison camp. When the site was visited by the U.S. Vice Presidential party in July 1959, it was evident that the Beloyarskoye plant was way behind schedule, for the concrete base was just being poured. The party was told that the plant was scheduled to be completed in 1961 and that the capacity at that time would correspond only to the original goal of 200 megawatts. There was some indication that the station might be expanded after that date.

Although their first power reactor was of the GVF type, the Soviets seem not to have a strong preference for it, for at least two of their stations will be both moderated and cooled by water under pressure. These are of the PWR type (in Soviet terminology, VVR), which has received major emphasis in the United States. In 1959 construction of the VVR station was started at the village of Novovoronezhskaya (near Voronezh on the Don River) in the northeast Ukraine. Like Beloyarskoye, its initial rating will be 210 megawatts gross, with that figure perhaps being doubled later.[2, 3] A similar plant was to have been constructed near Leningrad but its status as of the summer of 1959 was completely unknown.

The third type of atomic power station is that which has been developed by members of the Thermotechnical Laboratory working under the direction of A. I. Alikhanov. It is a reactor moderated by heavy water (D_2O), cooled by carbon dioxide gas. Although some information indicated that a 300-megawatt plant of this type would be built in the Soviet Union, there is no recent information to indicate that this is so. Instead, the same type of plant is being constructed by Soviet experts in Czechoslovakia. This will be a 150-electrical-megawatt unit located on the river Hron near Banská-Bystrica. Plans for a similar station in Russia may therefore have been abandoned, but this station may some day emerge again as did the "fifth." But, although the Czech plant was largely Soviet designed and built, it seems unreasonable that such a plant should be reckoned as part of the goals for installation of atomic power in the Soviet Union.

In addition to the three major types of reactors described, another reactor test station will be established near Ul'yanovsk on the Volga to investigate several reactor concepts of an advanced type. The first installation at the test station will be a boiling-water-type reactor such as was pioneered at the Argonne National Laboratory in the United States. Its electrical output will be about 50 megawatts. A second experimental reactor will use a graphite moderator with molten sodium as a coolant. The third type of Soviet reactor, using a suspension of uranium oxide in heavy water as fuel, will be designed to breed uranium-233 from thorium-232. Successful operation of this reactor is regarded as a prelude to the construction of one rated at 300 to 500 electrical megawatts, but the latter is not projected under the current Plan.

A fourth type of reactor at the test station will be a fast breeder reactor (Soviet code: BR-50) that uses plutonium as the chain-reacting substance and uranium-238 as a breeding blanket. The reactor will use liquid sodium alloy as a coolant. The design of this reactor is based on experience gained in the operation since 1955 of several experimental fast reactors (nonelectrical) at the Institute of Physics of Glavatom, which is located at the site of the first Soviet atomic power plant. These include an advanced type, with a rating of 5 megawatts, that came into operation in the summer of 1958. The latter resembles somewhat a U.S. reactor, using enriched uranium, that came into operation in 1951. Looking beyond the operation of BR-50, Soviet physicists are designing a fast reactor (BN-250) with an electrical output of 250 megawatts in a phase beyond the current Plan. Similar programs, using enriched uranium and plutonium in fast breeder reactors, have been under way for some time in the United States and in Great Britain, but in the USSR there seems to be extensive emphasis on the use of plutonium.

The combined electrical output at the Soviet test station will be perhaps 200 megawatts. This total, combined with what little can be ascertained about the levels of the larger power plants, indicates that the original 2,000- to 2,500-megawatt goal may possibly have been extended toward the end of the Seven-Year Plan in 1965, i.e., a delay of three to five years. The Soviet atomic power program is subject to at least the same degree of variation as is any other nation's program, and this only serves to emphasize that matching kilowatt for kilowatt is not a valid tactic in running the atomic power race.

The chief engineer of the Beloyarskoye plant told Vice President Nixon: "We of the Soviet Union do not believe nuclear power is the most important way of obtaining electrical energy."* His statement and Mr. Kozlov's have a similar ring. Coupled with the evident cutback in the scheduling of their nuclear power plant plans, these statements indicate that while technical investigation is being conducted at a great rate, actual installation will proceed with caution.

In the variety of types being considered, the U.S. program is broader than the Soviets'. There is no Soviet development along the lines of the graphite-moderated, gas-cooled reactors upon which Britain has based her gigantic atomic power program and which, in terms of planned kilowatts, leads the world. But the Soviet program is a formidable one and possesses the inherent strength to intensify and race when desired. Undoubtedly, any similarities or differences in international atomic power programs must be correlated with necessary differences in economic outlook and the over-all future power plans that employ all the various means for producing energy.

There are valid reasons for expecting a resurgence of economic incentives for nuclear power at a later date. The great bulk of Soviet industry and population is concentrated in the European part of Russia. Four-fifths of the total power

* *Washington Post,* August 1, 1959, p. A6.

produced in the USSR is required by the European economy. This energy requirement is almost symmetrically reversed with respect to energy resources, for well over 70 per cent of the unexploited reserves of energy resources is to be found in the Asian part of the USSR. As the eastern regions become more industrialized and use a greater share of their domestic resources, the proportionate demand of the European part of the Soviet Union and the Urals will still be something like two-thirds of the total national power consumption figure. By that same time most of the hydroelectric resources in European Russia will have been tapped. If other sources of energy were not available, the rest of the demand would have to be met by conventional fuels. But because of the poor coal-bed conditions in the European part, the cost of mining coal there is increasing, and, in fact, is higher than the cost of coal production in Siberia. And the cost of transporting the cheaper Siberian coal to regions of greatest demand is prohibitively high.

Several areas in the USSR possess abundant supplies of power but little industry as yet to use that power. Essentially, atomic fuels must be thought of as highly concentrated fuels, that is, as packaged power. If processed in areas where power is cheap and plentiful, nuclear fuels can then be shipped at very low cost to those areas where power is required.

In December 1957, Academician A. A. Blagonravov espoused the need for small atomic power plants on mobile caterpillar tracks to serve important areas of the far north. And it was evident that work on such plants was well under way by then, for a year later an experimental mobile unit was to be tested at the Institute of Physics of Glavatom. Some localities are so isolated and so poorly endowed by nature that no domestic power resources are available and it is uneconomical to transport large amounts of energy to those regions. A good example is the diamond fields in western

Yakutia, just west of the Lena River and right on the Arctic Circle. Apparently the deposits that have been found there rival those in South Africa and will enable the Soviet Union to become independent of outside diamond supplies. However, the area in which they are found is among the most desolate in the USSR. In some locations power is available only at the cost of as much as two rubles, or approximately forty cents, per kilowatt hour. This is about one hundred times the normal cost of industrial power. While present atomic energy costs from small so-called packaged power reactors are very high, they in no way compare with the two-ruble figure. It is possible then that the small atomic energy plants under development in the USSR are close to being economically feasible for these remote locations at the present time.

13

THE MOBILE ATOM

It is interesting to note that the subject of atomic energy for propulsion seems as controversial a political and technical problem in the USSR as it is in the United States. Simply because a particular U.S. technical program is bogged down by internal controversy, it does not always follow that the way may be clear in another country, particularly in the USSR, for the rapid and satisfactory solution of that problem. Nor is the contrary always the case.

The major problem in using atomic energy to propel one type of vehicle or another is that of shielding. For in a manned vehicle it is necessary to protect the passengers from the dangerous nuclear radiation that always accompanies large-scale atomic power units. In both manned and unmanned vehicles, electronic and physical materials are subject to radiation damage. Although there are various methods for minimizing radiation effects, all of these schemes require large amounts of bulk weight, and it is not likely that this weight penalty will ever be substantially reduced.

Although there is a great deal in the popular Soviet press on atomic propulsion, there is practically no information to indicate how advanced the Soviets really are in that field. It is pertinent, then, to look at some of the technical developments in this field, even though Soviet writers do not identify their contributions as such. Early in 1950, one of Igor Kurchatov's groups began the construction of a nuclear reactor in which shielding materials and other materials might be tested. A first test stand, although not a reactor, was operated in the spring of 1950 to obtain certain experimental parameters necessary for the test reactor itself. During the course of this work it was decided to build two reactors, one to test shielding materials and the second to test other properties of the materials. The latter reactor, known as the Reactor for Physical and Technical Investigations (RFT), was completed in March 1952 and started operating in April 1952. No starting date has been publicly released for the shielding reactor.[1] However, it is reasonable to assume that since its development was parallel to that of the RFT reactor the shielding reactor went into operation at about the same time. It is pertinent to note that the U.S. materials-testing reactor, which in function is the counterpart of the RFT, went into operation at almost exactly the same time, on March 31, 1952. Just as the U.S. bulk shielding reactor and materials-testing reactors were important to studies on the submarine propulsion reactor, the Soviet reactors could have been (but were not necessarily) intended for a similar development purpose. The same type of reactor is also needed in the development of industrial atomic power plants.

The experimental atomic power station of the USSR went into nuclear operation on May 9, 1954, and first produced electricity on June 27 of that year. The power plant is a direct extension of the RFT reactor but, more significantly, it is not much different from a type of reactor that is adaptable to marine or submarine propulsion problems. In the United States a pressurized-water reactor (the PWR) is currently favored for propulsion applications. The Soviet atomic power station uses pressurized water as a coolant, but is moderated by graphite. There is an extensive Soviet PWR development program, but this was not revealed until two years after their power station was unveiled. The latter may represent an abandoned technology as far as nuclear propulsion is concerned. Thus there is a possibility, but no proof, that the prototype power station was initially built for purposes other than purely for generating industrial electrical power.

The most obvious application to which these reactors might have been directed is the propulsion of nuclear submarines. The first nuclear submarine in the world was the *Nautilus,* which was launched on January 21, 1954, without having all of its nuclear equipment installed. About a year later, it was undergoing sea trials under nuclear power. The *Nautilus* was the forerunner of a growing family of nuclear submarines. Although there is much speculation in the popular Soviet press about nuclear submarines, there is no published evidence that the USSR possesses one. But it is important to note that Soviet fleet emphasis has long been on submarine warfare, and the USSR Navy possesses an extensive component of conventional submarines (an active fleet of 475, compared with 110 active in the U.S. fleet).[2] Numerous articles in Soviet military and naval media show that the possible advantages of nuclear undersea craft are appreciated. One Soviet naval expert wrote in 1955: "Submarines with atomic engines can cover enormous distances concealed, and approach, undetected, hostile ships, ports and bases, and deal them surprise blows. Especially notable will be such blows by submarines using atomic weapons."[3]

In view of this philosophy, it would be prudent to conclude, as has the Undersea Warfare Advisory Panel of the U.S. Joint Committee on Atomic Energy, that

We must assume that the Soviets will soon possess nuclear submarines which can fire ballistic missiles. The threat from the sea against our cities may assume completely new, and more ominous, dimensions beginning about 1962. . . . Their capability in this area should increase rapidly thereafter.[4]

One might further hypothesize that if the shielding and RFT reactors were parts of the atomic submarine development program, the Soviets might have chosen for their first power-producing reactor one that would at the same time provide further information on propulsion and serve as a prototype for their nuclear power program. It would make some sense to proceed in this manner instead of putting their first "Model T" reactor directly in a submarine, for they might feel that a few years' experience would make their first atomic submarine obsolete. It should be noted that the launching of the *Nautilus* and that of the Soviet atomic power station were approximately coincident.

If and when the existence of Soviet nuclear submarines is officially revealed, they are likely to be coupled to such "peaceful" uses as oceanographic research and cable-laying. A recent Soviet pamphlet on the subject ascribes only a military intent on the part of the United States and suggests that nuclear submarines would only be used for benign purposes by the Soviets.

Another military application of atomic propulsion is in the field of aviation. In the United States this has been a subject of much political maneuvering, the issue appearing to be whether one should (1) provide a "Model T" type of aircraft regardless of utility for the purposes of prestige or world-wide political effect or (2) concentrate on the long-range development of a military aircraft having advanced operational utility. On the basis of actual and inferred Soviet behavior in the extremely costly field of nuclear development, one would guess that the Soviets have chosen to follow the second course. A major article by Peter Kapitsa on "Some Problems of Organizing Scientific Work" appeared in *Pravda* on May 4, 1957, and indicated that a cautious, well-organized approach is being urged. Kapitsa said:

A characteristic feature of the scientific and industrial research institutes is the organization of their research work according to fields of knowledge. Until recently, such organization satisfied life's demands.

In the past decade, however, life has increasingly posed the need for solving big scientific and technical problems that embrace several fields of knowledge. Take, for example, an atomic-powered airplane: its creation requires atomic physicists and specialists in heat and power engineering and in aerodynamics, not to mention designers, metallurgists and others.

It is, of course, entirely possible that the Soviets made their decision some time before the United States did and may therefore be the first to claim a nuclear aircraft as an operational reality. Despite strong suggestions of military interest by such men as Chief Marshal of Aviation P. F. Zhigarev and Marshal K. Vershinin, there are no published data to indicate actual Soviet progress in nuclear aircraft propulsion. However, if the Soviets are embarked upon an atomic aircraft program, a reasonable description of their expected status in 1959 is provided by the *Financial Times* of London:

Russian work in this field can be described only in less detail, but it is known to be far advanced. Not only has an aircraft carrying a reactor furnace been in flight for the last three years, but an entirely new nuclear powered unit for an aircraft designed by the Tupolev team which created the

TU 114 air liner has been trial tested experimentally on the ground.

The reactor furnace used heats the air to an extent where the ducts carrying it away must be able to withstand temperatures of the order of 1,650 to 1,850 degrees Fahrenheit. These ducts are made of special steels.[5]

The reactor furnace mentioned would not actually propel the carrying aircraft, but would be used to collect data about crew-shielding, materials behavior under flight stress, and so on. A B-36 aircraft has carried a reactor to provide data for the U.S. aircraft propulsion program.

Another indication of heightened Soviet interest about 1956–57 is a very interesting text published by the Popular Science Library of the Military Publishing House of the Department of Defense in September 1957. It is entitled *The Application of Atomic Engines in Aviation.* Although it does not reveal anything that might be considered to be of a secret nature, it does provide a very comprehensive text for the engineer on the possible modes of achieving nuclear-powered flight. The text makes a claim to Soviet priority in this field by referring to a 1935 article by the Soviet scientist O. Petrovskii, who described a model of an aircraft that would operate on the energy from nuclear fusion. Aware of the shielding problem at that time, Petrovskii solved it by suggesting that the nuclear components be towed at some distance behind the aircraft itself.

Regardless of the status of their submarine or aircraft programs, the Soviet Union has on the seas a nuclear-powered ship. It is their icebreaker, *The Lenin,* which was launched on December 5, 1957, in the Leningrad shipyards before its nuclear components were fitted. The latter phase was completed in about ten months and the icebreaker was undergoing pre-operational tests in 1959. *The Lenin* is powered by three nuclear reactors which impart to the main generators a maximum capacity of 44,000 horsepower. *The Lenin* will be able to ply the northern sea routes for periods of about a year at full power without refueling. Under normal conditions, two of the reactors will be operating; the third will be used only when heaviest ice conditions are encountered. A staff of "specialist-physicists" will be aboard to supervise the complex reactor controls.

Conventional icebreakers are able to perform their tasks for only about one month before refueling. Clearly, in the desolate Arctic wastes, the atomic icebreaker will have a definite advantage. The construction of more icebreakers for use on rivers and large inland reservoirs is also being planned.

The nuclear "heart" of *The Lenin* is a pressurized-water reactor of almost the same type as that powering the U.S. submarine *Nautilus*. Its nuclear power plant may have been already well developed for a classified function such as the propulsion of a submarine. In any event, *The Lenin* is now clear evidence of that capability. However, the "father" of the *Nautilus,* Admiral Rickover, after inspecting *The Lenin* on July 27, 1959, concluded: "I think they realized that we are far ahead of them in the production of atomic-powered vessels." But Admiral Rickover was not entirely negative, for he stated: "I think they have done a fine and creditable job. The equipment is good, and, although it is difficult to estimate its efficiency at this stage, the design is adequate for their purposes."[6]

It is doubtful that there are strong motives for Soviet construction of large ocean-going vessels or merchant ships, since this has never been a strong point in their conventional maritime policy. Popular and technical discussion of such ships exists, but there is no indication of official interest.

That there is more than a superficial Soviet interest in the problems of nuclear propulsion is indicated by the creation in 1954 of the Institute of Complex Transportation

Problems at Moscow.* The importance of the Institute was evidently enhanced by the directive of the Twentieth Party Congress in February 1956, which read: "Begin work for setting up atomic-powered apparatus for transport purposes. Construct a nuclear-powered icebreaker."[7]

The appellation "Complex" may be almost synonymous with "atomic," since this seems to be a major interest of the Institute. The bulk of the Institute's work seems to be concerned more with the associated logistical studies and economies of coupling of conventional transport systems to atomic cores than with work on the development of atomic reactors themselves. The Director, Tirgan Sergeyevich Khachaturov, is a well-known economist specializing in transportation problems.

The Institute is also considering nuclear propulsion for locomotives and automobiles. For example, they note that only a few grams of uranium would be needed to operate the average-sized Soviet car, the Pobeda, for 62,000 miles, instead of the 12 to 15 tons of petrol usually required. But the great practical difficulties attending these applications can be related to the radiation problem. Even if it were possible to overcome the weight aspect, the normal incidence of train and automobile accidents would seem to present the problem of radioactive contamination from damaged atomic motors, and it is doubtful if the Institute has made great progress toward an atomic automobile.

A study on atomic locomotion that received considerable Western notice did not come from the Institute of Complex Transportation Problems but originated as a student's thesis from the Bauman Higher Technical School at Moscow. The study was based on Western data and should not be taken as any indication of a serious Soviet atomic locomotion project.

* At Nizhnaya Krasnosel'skaya Ulitsa, No. 39, in the northeast sector of the city.

The Institute regards the electrification of railway power lines by means of atomic power stations as more meaningful than an atomic locomotive.

What is more interesting, however, is the fact that students are encouraged to look into problems such as these and to use their imaginations in projecting future applications of atomic energy. Indeed, all segments of the Russian public and specialized audiences are stimulated to think about extremely advanced problems. To take an example from the propulsion field, Y. Balabanov, Doctor of Physical Mathematical Sciences, has discussed the problem of driving aircraft with thermonuclear motors, using certain ionic propulsion techniques that seem to be developing in the thermonuclear research program (see Chapter 19).

Herein seems to lie an important bit of Soviet philosophy: if a particular scientific development is foreseeable but seems to be particularly remote, there is a definite advantage in publicizing those concepts to encourage ideas that might make such developments less remote. Perhaps here is a philosophy that Western classification experts would do well to ponder carefully.

14

"BUY USEFUL ISOTOPES!"

The most versatile atomic tool for almost every experimenter in all of the sciences is the radioactive isotope that, with the aid of the radiation detector, can be used to trace physical and biological processes. More and more radioactive tracer studies have been conducted since the beginning of the century. The first investigators were limited by the few appropriate radioactive isotopes that could be found in nature, and later by the several that could be manufactured in extremely small amounts by accelerating machines such as the cyclotron.

One of the most ambitious early radioisotope programs was undertaken in 1940 by the All-Union Institute for Experimental Medicine, which constructed a radioisotope laboratory with the aid of scientists from the Lebedev Institute at Moscow. In that same year, the All-Union Institute ordered from the Ukrainian Physico-Technical Institute the construction of a linear accelerator to produce radioisotopes for their medical and biological research. However, most of this work was terminated by the onset of World War II.

With the coming of the nuclear reactor, it became possible to obtain fantastically large amounts of radioactive isotopes in considerable variety. Radioactive isotopes were manufactured in the first Soviet reactor, but because of its extremely low power and because of its low priority in relation to other studies, isotopes could not have been available at that time in any great amount. As the more powerful Soviet nuclear reactors came into operation, isotopes began to be used on a very wide scale throughout the USSR. Radioisotope laboratories have been built in higher educational institutes at Moscow, Leningrad, Kiev, Gorki, Kharkov, and Minsk. They are also used in numerous industrial laboratories in those areas and in the most remote areas of Uzbekistan, Kazakhstan, and in the Latvian Republic. They are used in medical and industrial laboratories from Archangel to Vladivostok, and on the Arctic ice island research station, "North Pole—5." In 1955, the total number of shipments of radioactive isotopes to various areas of Russia amounted to 1,500 packages per month. This may be compared with approximately 900 per month for that same year shipped by the Atomic Energy Commission to users in the United States. By the first quarter of 1957, the Russian monthly average had risen to 2,250 packages.

The over-all technical aspects of the Soviet isotope program are supervised by the Chief Directorate for the Utilization of Atomic Energy of the Council of Ministers. However, distribution is arranged by a state All-Union Trust, Soyuzreaktiv,* of the Ministry of Chemical Industry. Occasional newspaper advertisements are taken by Soyuzreaktiv to plug its products. "Buy Useful Isotopes!" they proclaim. A slick-

* May be addressed at Krivokolenny Pereulok, 12, Moscow.

paper prospectus with an accompanying price list is periodi-
cally issued by Soyuzreaktiv, listing over five hundred different compounds of specific isotopes. This catalogue bears
some similarity to the one issued by the AEC Oak Ridge
operation. However, there is no exact correspondence between certain isotopes that are available from the Soviet
agency and from Oak Ridge. Regarding prices, it should be
noted that the ruble/dollar ratios for the same isotope are
generally less for those isotopes produced by neutron beam
irradiation in a reactor than for those that must be separated
from fission products. This might indicate that in the USSR
there is an abundance of atomic reactor facilities with what
is termed "high reactivity" (that is, lots of excess neutrons)
as compared with the number of such facilities in the United
States. But this comparison cannot be made with certainty,
since Russian commodity prices are artificially established.

The Soyuzreaktiv catalogue also lists the stable isotopes
that must be separated from a mixture of isotopes found in
the artificial state. This separation of stable isotopes seems
to have been pioneered in the USSR by a group in the Institute of Atomic Energy and by other groups of Soviet scientists working with captive German specialists.

Two of the German scientists are given major credit for
developing some of the techniques. This is indeed unusual,
for the Soviets would prefer to have the West believe that the
Soviet atomic energy program developed entirely on the basis
of native talents. So the credits are hidden in papers authored
by Soviet scientists. Manfred von Ardenne is credited with
the development (in 1950) of special ion sources for use in
separation mass spectrometers. Gustav Hertz, who conceived
the notion of using gas diffusion for separation processes, led
a German-Soviet group during 1946–52 in the development
of several diffusion types of isotope separation. As a non-
Soviet citizen, Hertz can claim the unique distinction of

having been awarded both the Nobel and Stalin prizes. Hertz
and von Ardenne have now been repatriated to direct the
East German atomic energy program.

There are now in the Soviet Union over a dozen large-
scale isotope separators, operating on the electromagnetic
principle, to provide research institutions with a wide variety
of stable isotopes. During a five-month period in 1958, over
100 isotope shipments were made from the separators of the
Institute of Atomic Energy alone.

As for specific uses of isotopes, it would be impossible to
label any of the USSR or Western applications as unique,
for it is in this field of atomic energy that there seems to be
unlimited exchange of information by all scientists concerned. Information on isotopes was the first to "unfreeze"
(about August 1953) in the USSR, and there has been an
uninterrupted flow ever since. Scientists everywhere have
been quick to adapt a particular isotope process as soon as
it has been publicized.

At an international meeting held in April 1957 at Moscow, and at the Second Geneva Conference in 1958, representatives from a wide variety of Soviet industries discussed
the ways in which they are putting isotopes to use. Scientists
from the silk industry research institutes told how they are
using radiations from isotopes to change the sex of silkworms,
to preserve their cocoons, and to remove static charges as the
silk is being processed. (Irradiation of raw silk produces a
stronger, better knitting silk than does the usual heat treat-
ment of cocoons.) The fur institutes use radiation to measure
hair depth of fur pelts, and the shoe-leather institutes measure
the thicknesses of raw and cured leather by means of radiation. The milk industry uses isotopes for automatic regula-
tion of a number of the production processes, and the
USSR River Fleet employs radioactive isotopes as soil gauges
for suction dredgers in checking water levels in the Moscow-

Volga Canal and for corrosion studies on mechanical components of ships. In addition to the small radioactive isotope sources there are available large sources that have an equivalent strength up to 20,000 grams or more of radium. These large sources are used in medical institutions for therapeutical purposes, by food research institutes for preservation of food, by the rubber industry for vulcanization of rubber, and for the polymerization of certain plastics.

There is considerable interest in using radioactive isotopes for special power purposes. While the cost of electricity generated by such "atomic electric batteries" may usually be prohibitive, their use—though uneconomical—may be justified by the importance and urgency of specific applications. For future earth satellites, it is projected to use atomic batteries weighing from 110 to 115 kilograms, generating 100 watts of electricity. Strontium-90 is contemplated as one of the energy sources. Since this isotope has a half-life of 27 years, the sputnik would be powered effectively throughout its useful life span.

Nature also produces her own radioactive substances in the atmosphere, the most abundant of which is carbon-14. The use of the extremely small amounts of carbon-14 as tracers in archeology, biology, and other sciences was pioneered by W. F. Libby at the University of Chicago, and the Soviets have been quick to adopt his method in special carbon-14 laboratories.

All of these applications, which are merely illustrative and do not pretend to encompass the vast scope of radioisotope application in the USSR, must be backed up by an industry that produces instrumentation for the proper use of isotopes. Many items of equipment that the Soviets have displayed at international fairs and at their atomic pavilion in Moscow are commonly available and are often advertised in the newspapers. There are institutes to draft specifications for instruments that have a specialized or particular application. Generally available to industry, however, are the services of the Laboratory of Atomic Instruments, which is a branch of the All-Union Instrument Research Institute. Factories or other institutes having particular problems in the application of isotopes can request the assistance of the Laboratory of Atomic Instruments.

Thus, the use of isotopes is given maximum encouragement in the USSR, resulting, for example, in a saving for the national economy of 1.5 billion rubles in 1957 (compared with a U.S. figure of $500 million). And, while they are perhaps not as spectacular as nuclear reactors or gigantic accelerators, isotopes have a vast economic and medical potential that should not be underrated.

15

MATERIAL RESOURCES

Any atomic energy program must have as its basis an abundance of accessible uranium-bearing ores. The most celebrated USSR deposits are found in the Fergana Valley in the Central Asian Republics of Kirghizstan and Tadzhikstan, where in 1940 the Special Committee on the Problem of Uranium sent an expedition to appraise their extent. In the pre–World War II period, these deposits had been mined for their radium content and the then-useless uranium was simply dumped. The main centers of mining at that time were near the villages of Tyuya-Muyun and Taboshar.

Since the war, Soviet geologists have carried out an extensive program of uranium prospecting throughout the USSR. However, the locations and richness of the various deposits are guarded almost as zealously as the atomic bomb stockpile figures. In fact, no published information is available to indicate the extent of the internal USSR uranium deposits. USSR geologists at international meetings do not respond to questions regarding location.

The Soviets, however, obtain a good fraction of their uranium from abroad, chiefly in several of the satellite countries. As soon as the war with Germany was concluded, Russian geologists under the direction of Colonel General I. A. Serov (the recently deposed head of the Committee of State Security, KGB, and an old hand in secret police work) went into the uranium-rich Saxony region of Germany. This "Geologic Prospecting Group No. 1" was able to confirm the presence of tempting ore bodies. However, since the region at that time was occupied by American troops, it was impossible to proceed with the prospecting. When the U.S. troops retreated from the Elbe to the agreed lines of zone demarcation, Soviet geologists followed and initiated exploitation of the uranium deposits in Saxony. Further expansion occurred in 1946 with the appointment of a high secret police official, Major General Mikhail Mitrofanovich Mal'tsev, to head the operation under the code name "Wismut A. G.," which means bismuth in German. A decree dated July 17, 1947, formally established the East German Corporation of Wismut. This date again confirms that June 1947 was the critical decision period in the Soviet atomic energy program. Although highly secret at first, the existence of such a large operation in Germany could not possibly have been kept hidden, and there have since appeared occasional references to the activities of the organization in East German newspapers.

Another important source of Russian uranium has been Czechoslovakia, where, by means of forced labor, uranium has been mined in the Joachimsthal area of western Czechoslovakia and in the Pribram region of central Bohemia. The Joachimsthal mines are six hundred years old and for centuries were exploited as sources of silver and lead. After the discovery of radium, the site became an important production center for that material. In fact, Madame Curie's initial experiments were performed with Joachimsthal ore. It was natural that the Soviets would covet the uranium content of the mines after World War II. The deposits are still producing and, for the most part, are now under the direction of Czechoslovak experts. In the past few years, Czechoslovakia has negotiated a price with the Soviet Union, and it is claimed that the uranium is sold under the same conditions that Belgian Congo uranium is sold to the United States.

Other deposits of uranium are being exploited in Poland, Rumania, and Hungary. In the latter country, the uranium miners at Pecs were among the first to strike in the general revolt of 1956. Because of possible instabilities in the satellite uranium situation, and because of the general drive toward self-sufficiency, the development of domestic USSR sources continues. There have been many indications that the number of deposits thus far found in the USSR is not deemed to be satisfactory to meet the expanding needs of the Soviet atomic weapons and power programs, and that the Russians envy the West its vast uranium resources. For example, a 1955 book by A. A. Santalov entitled *The Imperialist Struggle for Raw Material Resources* charged that the United States was monopolizing the non-Communist world supply of uranium, and soon after publication of the book, *Pravda* echoed the same charge in stronger terms.

Since the announcement of the Sixth Five-Year Plan in 1956 (now revised), Petr Yakovlevich Antropov, the Minister of Geology and Preservation of Resources of the USSR, has been publicly urging the expansion of exploration for rare minerals, including uranium. In articles titled "Search for Uranium!" the Ministry spokesmen have been urging young people to look everywhere on their hunting, fishing, and camping trips for uranium. "Look in old quarries and under your houses." Geiger counters (in Russian parlance, "radiometer indicators") have been furnished the Young Pioneer groups by the Ministry. However, there has been some criticism that the instruments are not sufficiently available. Of course, more extensive and complex prospecting, which includes the use of survey aircraft, has been carried out by the Ministry. What has been discovered is not likely to be published.

Never neglecting an opportunity to assert priority, the Soviets claim the discovery of a number of new uranium-bearing minerals, although they are reluctant to state where the minerals can be found. In 1947 the minerals gidronasturan (hydronasturan) and urgite were claimed. In 1952 a new silicate-type uranium mineral was named "nenadkevite" for Soviet geochemist K. A. Nenadkevich. In 1953 there appeared natrootenite. Now, even a nineteenth-century poet is enshrined in the annals of Soviet atomic mineralogy in the naming of a uranium-phosphate ore "lermontovite," after Mikhail Lermontov. Lermontov is often styled as the "Poet of the Caucasus"; perhaps it is not too risky to surmise that lermontovite is also native to that area. The mineral probably originates near Mount Mashuk, which supplies the resort city of Pyatigorsk with its renowned radioactive waters, and whose slopes were the scene of Lermontov's final duel.

An indication of Soviet Russia's intent in exploiting uranium resources to the fullest extent is provided by its interesting work in extracting uranium from natural lake waters. The uranium content of such waters is exceedingly low, but the comparative ease of extracting it from such a source has led Soviet geologists to conclude that this process is more economical than that of processing several types of poor uranium ores. A semi-industrial-scale operation for extraction from water was initiated during 1952–53.

Much of the work in the identification of the new minerals is performed by the Moscow Institute of the Geology of Ore Deposits (IGEM).[1] Prospecting and identification instrumentation is developed by several institutes. One of the more interesting developments for rapid ore assay as it comes from the mines is a special apparatus called the "Stationary Radiometer Control" (RKS), which is placed on the tracks carrying the wagons of ore from the mines. The bulk radiation from the ores serves to indicate the uranium content. This apparatus has been under continuous development since 1946, and is apparently used extensively in Soviet uranium operations.

The other main atomic energy material is thorium, which, after appropriate processing and irradiation in a nuclear reactor, can be changed to a fissionable material, uranium-233. Thorium has not been extensively used yet in atomic energy programs. However, the Soviets have shown an intense interest in the mineral; and since they have carried out thorough metallurgical research on thorium and have performed the requisite measurements on its nuclear properties, it is assumed that at the appropriate stage the Soviet thorium resources will be developed, if they have not been up to the present time.

There are other resources involved in atomic energy programs. In processing most of the materials, the main problem is to eliminate impurities that will capture neutrons in a nuclear reactor and thus be detrimental to the operation of the reactor. The purity problem is most critical in the manufacture of the nuclear fuel and the moderator materials. One of the common moderators is graphite, which is found in a natural state. However, natural graphite is difficult to purify and does not possess certain other requisite properties pertaining to density. It is therefore necessary for the atomic program to make artificial graphite from petroleum pitch. The existence of a number of nuclear reactors using graphite moderators in the USSR is proof enough that the barriers in manufacturing artificial graphite have been overcome. Substantial amounts of graphite will be required for the USSR atomic power stations. This is now the basis of a thriving small industry in the USSR.

Another important moderator material is beryllium, which has some promise for future families of nuclear reactors. In the USSR, beryllium production has been developed and an experimental nuclear critical assembly was actually built in 1954 using a beryllium moderator. This material is also being alloyed with magnesium as a cladding for certain fuel elements.

Heavy water, another moderating substance, which is present to the extent of one part in 6,000 in ordinary water, has been used extensively in the USSR. There are many methods of obtaining heavy water from natural water. One way is to use electrolysis and catalysis in conjunction with the operation of nitrogen fertilizer plants. This was the process used during the war at Trail, British Columbia, to obtain heavy water for the U.S. project. Electrolysis was the method used in the USSR at Chirchik in Central Asia before World War II and at Dniepropetrovsk to obtain small amounts of heavy water for experimental purposes. Recently Kurchatov has praised the development by the Institute of Physical Problems of a method of using low-temperature rectification of hydrogen for obtaining heavy water. This method was described in greater detail at the 1958 Geneva Conference by both Soviet and U.S. scientists. The low-temperature distillation method had been under development in the USSR since 1946, and a large-scale production plant has been operating now for several years. Production of heavy water in the USSR is not confined to this method, and Kurchatov has stated: "We now produce deuterium on an industrial scale by various methods."

Several institutes in the USSR are devoted to problems of rare materials, some of which have application to the atomic energy program. Three of these organizations are the Institute of Mineralogy, Geochemistry, and Crystal Chemistry of Rare Elements; the Scientific Research Institute of Rare and Scarce Elements (at Moscow); and the Irkutsk Scientific Research Institute of Rare Metals. However, when a technology of a rare metal has to be developed for the atomic energy program, this work is usually carried out by one or more of the institutes directly engaged in atomic energy work. For example, the Moscow Engineering Physics Institute has done extensive research on the metallurgy of thorium, zirconium, and niobium alloys. As in any country embarked on a large-scale atomic energy program, there exists in the USSR a broad network of supplementary institutes and industries, each receiving direction from a strong central ministry and a few key research institutes.

16

THE ORGANIZATION AND
THE INSTITUTES

The first Chief Directorate of the Council of Ministers under the direction of Boris Lvovich Vannikov continued to exercise over-all direction of the Soviet atomic energy program until the day that Lavrentii Beria, head of the secret police, was arrested on June 26, 1953. As Vannikov's wartime and post-wartime superior, Beria controlled the atomic energy program within the Politburo. Vannikov, in his munitions post, had been dominated by Beria during World War II. It was a control of terror, as has been graphically illustrated by Victor Kravchenko:

With the outbreak of war, the Armaments and Munitions Commissariats had been placed under control of Beria, Commissar of the NKVD, who was also Assistant Chairman of the Sovnarkom and a member of the State Defense Committee. This amounted to putting them under the control of the secret police. The nominal Commissars, Oustinov and Vannikov, knew what it meant; so did everyone else, down to the lowliest official. They would have preferred a quick death to the righteous anger of Beria and his organization. Everyone in the plants and offices and institutions directly or indirectly connected with armaments and munitions was gripped by dread fear.

Beria was no engineer. He was placed in control for the precise purpose of inspiring deadly fear. I often asked myself —as others assuredly did in their secret hearts—why Stalin had decided to take this step. I could find only one plausible answer. It was that he lacked faith in the patriotism and national honor of the Russian people and was therefore compelled to rely primarily on the whip. Beria was his whip.[1]

On January 7, 1956, the Peoples' Commissariat of Munitions became a titularly "peaceful" organization as the Peoples' Commissariat of Agricultural Machine Construction, with Vannikov still in charge—and Beria supervising. So it was natural that secret police control should continue after Vannikov relinquished his ministerial duties to assume responsibility for the atomic energy program.

It is a simple matter to trace the beginning of a general lessening of tensions within the Soviet atomic energy program to the very date of Beria's arrest. On that day, the atomic energy Directorate was elevated to the status of a Ministry, that is, the Ministry of Medium Machine Building,[2] and put under the direction of Vyacheslav A. Malyshev. Vannikov was given the post of Malyshev's First Deputy. On February 28, 1955, Malyshev was promoted to the higher post of directing a number of Ministries for the Council of Ministers and three months later became head of a new Committee for the Council of Ministers for New Technology. It is believed that this committee, called "Gostekhnika," exercised strong general direction in all major USSR technical problems, but its exact influence on the atomic energy program is unknown. In May 1957 this committee was replaced by a group called the "State Scientific-Technical Committee," headed by Y. Y. Maksarev (appointed July 5, 1957).

With Malyshev's promotion, the Ministry of Medium Machine Building came under the control of Colonel General Avaamii Pavlovich Zavenyagin, a former deputy director of Beria's Ministry of Internal Affairs. Zavenyagin's industrial career had been most impressive; in the 1930's he had developed the Magnitogorsk Steel Combine in the Urals and other installations in Siberia. On New Year's Eve, 1956, Zavenyagin died at the age of 55 of coronary thrombosis. Vannikov eulogized the departed Minister on behalf of his fellow workers at the Ministry of Medium Machine Building. Zavenyagin's death marked the beginning of several organizational crises within the Soviet atomic energy program; Malyshev, who exercised technical control on a higher level, was afflicted with leukemia. Although very competent Soviet medical scientists were available, a West German specialist was called in to treat Malyshev secretly, perhaps for political reasons. Under these peculiar circumstances, Malyshev died on February 20, 1957.

After Zavenyagin's death, Mikhail G. Pervukhin, technical and economic expert of the Presidium, took over the post of Minister of Medium Machine Building. Later, during the period of the "anti-state activities" of Malenkov, Molotov, and Kaganovich, Pervukhin was identified with the dissident group and was removed from most of his official positions, including that of Minister of Medium Machine Building.

In the meantime, since April 18, 1956, with the increased emphasis on peaceful uses of atomic energy, a sector of the Medium Machine Building Ministry had been split off to form a Chief Directorate attached to the Council of Ministers for the Utilization of Atomic Energy (Glavatom).* This Directorate was headed by Yefim Pavlovich Slavskii, who was elevated to the higher post of Minister of Medium Machine

---

* Glavatom may be addressed at Post Office Box 1024, Central Post Office, Moscow.

Building when Pervukhin was demoted. Boris Vannikov remained as First Deputy Minister; on December 30, 1957, in honor of his sixtieth birthday, and for services to the Soviet State and Soviet Army for the "development of new techniques," he was awarded the Order of Lenin, the highest state honor.

Slavskii, a Ukrainian and a member of the Communist Party since 1918, is a graduate of the Moscow Institute of Non-Ferrous Metals and Gold. After successfully directing two important aluminum factories, he became Deputy Minister of Non-Ferrous Metals before transferring to atomic energy work. Slavskii's replacement as head of Glavatom is Vasilii Semenovich Yemel'yanov, also a long-time Party member. Yemel'yanov is a 1927 graduate of the Moscow Mining Academy, and since 1935 he has occupied various posts of administrative responsibility. During World War II he was Chairman of the Committee of Standards. During this period, and up to the present time, Yemel'yanov has participated in metallurgical research projects and, in recent years, has published papers on a variety of atomic energy structural materials. Much of the later work has been performed at the Moscow Engineering Physics Institute, which has a significant role in the USSR atomic energy program. Yemel'yanov is fairly well known in the West, since for the past several years he has been the chief Soviet delegate to the International Atomic Energy Agency and to numerous international conferences. Yemel'yanov's deputy is Dmitrii Vasilievich Yefremov, who has held a number of important posts in the USSR electrical equipment industry. In April 1959 he received a Lenin prize for his role as chief engineer of the 10,000,000,000-volt synchrophasotron at Dubna. Thus the men who administer the Soviet atomic energy program belong to a unique breed of civil servants of the Soviet state. Developed over many decades, this high-level cadre of state servants is composed of hardened, devoted Communists combining technical, political, and administrative competence.

The actual sites where fissionable materials and nuclear weapons are manufactured must remain unknown until the Soviet leaders deign to tell the world of their locations. Now and then a hint does diffuse through the ferrous curtain to tell of some activity which might be connected with the production of fissionable materials. For example, in October 1957, listeners to the home service of Moscow Radio were treated to a report by a scientific observer who had just visited a field group of a geophysical laboratory of the Urals Branch of the USSR Academy of Sciences. This group was located on the shore of Lake Miass and was involved in the extremely interesting and pertinent problem of disposing of radioactive wastes and their effects on water organisms, plants, et cetera. In the United States most of the similar work is conducted near the great manufacturing centers of Hanford and Oak Ridge, where quanties of fission products would be easily and readily available. Can we conclude that there is a fissionable materials production center near Lake Miass (in Chelyabinsk Province), or is this an unwarranted assumption? Probably we shall never know, for Lake Miass is in a highly restricted section of the USSR, strictly forbidden to foreign travel, and, despite the concluding assertion of the commentator that this station is "devoted to the peaceful uses of atomic energy," no Westerner has ever been invited to it.

Meager information is available, however, on some of the installations that have developed the techniques and instrumentation for the secret manufacturing sites. Almost every higher technical institution—including the well-known ones such as the Institute of Physical Problems, the Lebedev Physics Institute, the Kurnakov Institute of General and Inorganic Chemistry, the Leningrad Physico-Technical Institute, the Ukrainian Physico-Technical Institute, and particularly the Radium Institute—has contributed to the atomic energy program according to its particular talents. It was also necessary to set up several highly specialized new institutions to attack the atomic energy problem as their primary and sole responsibility. Some of these will be described. The major research group is headed by Igor Vasilyevich Kurchatov. At the end of the war it was simply designated as "Laboratory No. 2 of the Academy of Sciences." On Kurchatov's staff, at that time, were such well-known people as S. L. Sobolev, M. S. Kozodaev, I. K. Kikoin, and G. N. Flerov. Kurchatov's Laboratory appears to have worked on practically every aspect of the Soviet atomic energy program. At an indeterminate date, approximately when the Soviets achieved their first atomic explosion, the title of Kurchatov's Laboratory was changed to the Laboratory for Measuring Instruments (abbreviated LIP), which was obviously a cover name conveying no meaning at all. But the trend toward revealing the Laboratory's true function continued, and in the period after Stalin's death the name was changed again to the Moscow Physical Institute. In official parlance, "institute" usually implies broader responsibilties than "laboratory," so that this change indicated a new importance for Kurchatov's group. Finally, following the demise of Zavenyagin, Kurchatov's Institute was given its proper appellation, The Institute of Atomic Energy (IAE).

Located in the western suburbs of Moscow, the Institute is an almost self-sufficient scientific community, having comfortable apartment accommodations for its staff members. It is divided into a number of specialized laboratories, including the much publicized Thermonuclear Laboratory of Lev Andreevich Artzimovich.

The research equipment at IAE consists of a 1.5-meter-diameter cyclotron (completed in 1946), electromagnetic isotope separators, and radioactivity "hot lab" facilities. Also on the site are the important 15- to 20-megawatt Reactor for Physical and Technical Research (RFT) and the 3-megawatt shielding reactor that are being used for design studies on the large-scale atomic power plants. On November 23, 1957, a "swimming pool" type of reactor (coded IRT) was put into operation by a visiting guest, Francis Perrin of France. Similar to a number of reactors in the West, IRT operates at about 2 megawatts and has become a prototype for versatile research reactors to be built at other institutes.

IAE collaborates with the other atomic energy institutes and laboratories. One of the most important joint efforts for the Soviet peaceful power program was a joint enterprise by Kurchatov of IAE with Anatolii Petrovich Aleksandrov, Director of the Institute of Physical Problems during the time when Kapitsa was in eclipse. Kurchatov and Aleksandrov are credited with the development, in the USSR, of the water-cooled atomic power reactor. This type of reactor forms a main basis of the USSR and U.S. peaceful power programs. Now that the directorship of his Institute has been restored to Kapitsa, Aleksandrov has become the head of Leningrad State University and is probably concerned with the construction of a large atomic power plant that is to be built near Leningrad, and with the naval propulsion units on which he reported at the Geneva Conference of 1958.

Another laboratory established for special purposes was A. I. Alikhanov's Thermotechnical Laboratory (south Moscow), which appears to have had tasks of a nature intermediate between those of Kurchatov's Institute, which was mainly concerned with atomic energy engineering, and those of the Dubna Institute, which worked almost entirely on pure research. The word "thermotechnical" has a slight relationship to the major problems of Alikhanov's Institute, which was initially directed toward the development of reactors having highly thermalized neutron spectra, that is, systems where the energy of the neutron is rapidly diminished, and toward thermalized neutron research. However, this was not the sole function of the Thermotechnical Laboratory. Extensive cosmic ray field work has been sponsored in the past by the Laboratory, although much of this work was transferred to other institutes after more specialized equipment relating to the atomic energy program became available. In addition to the neutron spectroscopy equipment, a heavy-water–moderated research reactor has been in operation since April 1949. Initially operated at a level of 500 kilowatts, it has recently been reconstructed to operate at 2 megawatts. This reactor served as a prototype for the research reactors supplied to China and Yugoslavia. There is also a small cyclotron (with a magnet diameter of about 40 inches) on the premises.

As a model for his gigantic 50-Bev* nuclear accelerator (see Chapter 18), V. V. Vladimirskii is building at the Thermotechnical Laboratory a 6- to 7-Bev "strong-focusing" synchrophasotron (a most impressive energy for a *model*), which should be fully operative about 1960. The March 1959 session of the Academy of Sciences of the USSR confirmed Alikhanov as the Director of the Institute of Theoretical and Experimental Physics. As was the case for the Institute of Atomic Energy, this evidently denotes a higher status for the Thermotechnical Laboratory and finally gives some recognition to the true function of Alikhanov's group.

During the war, there existed, under the direction of Van-

---

* An electron after falling across a potential difference of one volt has acquired an energy of one electron volt (ev). One million electron volts is abbreviated as Mev; similarly, one billion ev is abbreviated as Bev. Chemical energies are usually measured in terms of electron volts or less, while nuclear energies occur in quantities of thousands, millions, or even billions of electron volts.

nikov's Ministry of Munitions and therefore under Beria's control, a secret institute called the Moscow Mechanical Institute (MMI), which specialized in training students in the technical arts that are an adjunct to modern warfare. After the war, atomic energy was included in the curriculum of the MMI, and many of the prominent scientists from Kurchatov's and Alikhanov's laboratories and from other institutes became professors there. Of course, training in nuclear physics continued at all of the public institutions such as Moscow State University, but it was not the specialized, directed sort of training that was given at MMI. At least until 1949, MMI included in its curricula such subjects as "Construction of Munitions," "Technology and Provision of Munitions," and "Technology and Provision of Rocket Armaments." There is no published information after 1949 to indicate that subjects such as rocket technology are still taught at that Institute, but it is possible that they are. It can be reported, however, that atomic energy activities have continued to expand. And, in addition to its training functions, a large amount of essential atomic energy research has been done at the Institute. After 1953, when so many secret institutes were changing one cryptic title to another, the MMI became known as the Moscow Engineering Physics Institute (MIFI),* and much of the less "sensitive" atomic energy work that is being performed at MIFI today is unclassified and available in the open literature.

The Director of MIFI since 1956 has been Ivan Ivanovich Novikov, a specialist in thermodynamics and nuclear energetics. Born in 1916, Novikov is a man to watch. During 1954–56 he held the important post of Deputy Chief Scientific Secretary of the Presidium of the Academy of Sciences.

---

* Main office at 21 Kirova Ulitsa, several blocks northeast of the Kremlin.

He is chief editor of the Soviet atomic energy journal and was recently named director of an important new atomic energy institute in Siberia.

Educational handbooks for 1957 and 1958 list as MIFI specialties the following subjects: (1) Theoretical and Experimental Physics, (2) Physico-Energetics, (3) Physics Engineering, and (4) Mathematical Computing Equipment. Soviet authorities still are not completely candid on the function of the Institute, obvious as it might be from the scientific literature, and prospective students must have special information to apply. A high-ranking administrator of the USSR Academy of Sciences, D. Y. Panov, has claimed that the MIFI and the Massachusetts Institute of Technology are comparable institutions. This is an impressive comparison to make concerning a school so young.

Moscow State University and Leningrad State University are the larger higher educational centers and are well equipped to train nuclear scientists and technicians.

At Moscow State University, which is the largest educational establishment in the USSR, a research reactor using enriched uranium with ordinary water as moderator and coolant (given the Soviet code VVR-S) serves as a prototype for research reactors that are being provided to several of the Soviet bloc nations. Associated with the University is an Institute of Nuclear Physics.

For Leningrad, which has a number of nuclear research and training institutes, a versatile high-power research reactor of the water-moderated type has been provided. The reactor (coded VVR-M) is capable of producing radioisotopes of high specific activity and will be used for a wide range of reactor and irradiation studies.

Additionally, many of the regional institutes are receiving nuclear equipment. For example, the new Institute of Physics on the outskirts of Kiev is one of many centers being provided with small cyclotrons (which seem to have become stock items), an experimental nuclear reactor, and radioisotope laboratories. Twelve miles northeast of Tashkent, at Kibrai, the Uzbek Academy of Sciences has established an Institute of Nuclear Physics, having several special laboratories, and a reactor is being provided. Nuclear facilities, including a research reactor, have been installed for the institutes of the city of Sverdlovsk in the Urals. These are only a few of the nuclear research and training centers within the vast research complex of the USSR Academy of Sciences.

17

NEW CITIES

During World War II, three substantial "atomic cities"—
Hanford, Oak Ridge, and Los Alamos—were created in the
United States as secret centers for the development and manufacture of the atomic bomb. Immediately after the first
atomic bomb was dropped on Hiroshima, the existence of
the three cities became known, and two or three smaller
centers of weapons activity that have since been established
in Europe are also known to the rest of the world. Similar
communities, "the Atomgrads," which have been established
in the Soviet Union for the development and production of
bomb materials, have remained secret. Consequently, it is
not possible to describe their number, location, or function.
But several atomic communities for research of a less secret
nature have been, or are about to be, established in the USSR,
and a fair amount of information about them is available.

One of the intents of the Soviet security system in agree-

ing to relinquish information on some of the advanced research institutes is to give an impression that the existence
of all of the Russian "atomic cities" is being revealed. There
has never been even the vaguest public reference in the Russian press to the huge scientific and industrial complexes that
must be in existence to permit the Soviet Union to develop
and manufacture its atomic and hydrogen bombs.

The most publicized Russian atomic installation is located
at the newly named site of Dubna, north of Moscow, where
the Moscow-Volga Canal meets the Volga River. The history
of its establishment is as follows.

In early 1946 Mikhail Grigorievich Meshcheryakov, a
co-worker of Kurchatov's, was in the United States as a
Soviet representative at the disarmament discussions. Following his return from the Pacific, where he witnessed the
Bikini bomb tests, Meshcheryakov visited the Cyclotron Laboratory of the University of California at Berkeley. The
accelerator work being conducted at Berkeley seems to have
impressed Meshcheryakov, and evidently this was instrumental in a decision to build a similar machine, but of greater
power, in the USSR. The site selected was that of the village
of Ivankovo, north of Moscow, and construction was started
in 1947 on the cyclotron that is described in Chapter 18.
Subsequently, the site name was changed to Bolshaya Volga,
and later (about 1956) to Dubna.

Probably this change of name was coincidental with the
decision to establish the Dubna site as the Eastern Institute
for Nuclear Research, to be staffed by Soviet personnel and
scientists of eleven bloc countries. During March 1956 a
meeting was held to establish this institute. Evidently, the
term "Eastern" was not acceptable to one or more of the
delegate nations, and the title of the center emerged several
days later as the Joint Institute of Nuclear Research. The
agreement establishing the Institute provides that the laboratory containing Meshcheryakov's gigantic 680-Mev accel-

erator, and previously known as the Institute of Nuclear Problems of the USSR, should be relegated to the status of the Laboratory of Nuclear Problems of the Joint Institute of Nuclear Research. Similarly, the name of Vladimir Veksler's adjacent Electro-Physical Institute was to be changed to the High Energy Physics Laboratory, and the 10-Bev accelerator was transferred to Joint Institute use. Evidently, the two large accelerators were the only major pieces of equipment at the Dubna site. The articles of agreement further resolved that there should be established (a) a Laboratory of Theoretical Physics with a computing department and an electronic computing machine; (b) a Laboratory of Nuclear Problems with an experimental nuclear reactor having high-intensity neutron beams; (c) a cyclotron for accelerating multicharged ions of high atomic weight with helium (this cyclotron to be incorporated as part of the Laboratory of Nuclear Problems; (d) other unspecified laboratories and installations. Professor Dmitrii Ivanovich Blokhintsev, who is credited with directing the construction of the first Soviet atomic power station, has been named Director of the Joint Institute.

With the establishment of the Joint Institute, Meshcheryakov relinquished his post as Director of the defunct Institute of Nuclear Problems, and a former deputy director of that institute, V. P. Dzhelepov, took over as Director of the Laboratory of Nuclear Problems. Meshcheryakov continued to work as a member of Dzhelepov's group. Another leading member of the laboratory is Bruno M. Pontecorvo, who defected from Britain in September 1950. Pontecorvo has been working at the Dubna site ever since his defection, and has published some creditable experimental work in Soviet journals. He is now a Soviet citizen and a Lenin prize winner.

Veksler continued as Director of the new High Energy Physics Laboratory. The Director of the Laboratory of Theoretical Physics is Academician N. N. Bogolyubov, who has

recently aroused world-wide interest in his new theory of
phenomena that occur at temperatures close to absolute zero.
The Director of the Laboratory of Neutron Physics is Ilya N.
Frank, a corresponding member of the USSR Academy of
Sciences and a 1958 Nobel prize winner. It was in his laboratory that a new type of pulsed reactor was to be built. The
reactor would operate for extremely short periods at a time
(periods of the order of 15 millionths of a second), but during
that time would emit neutrons at an especially impressive
rate. A tunnel six-tenths of a mile long would be used for
experimentation with the pulsed neutrons from that apparatus, but there has been some difficulty connected with
the construction of this reactor and, as of the summer of
1957, the Director of the Joint Institute, Blokhintsev, stated
that the reactor was still in an idea stage, that it did not seem
at all promising, and that probably nothing would be done
with it. But later discussions in early 1959 indicated a renewed interest in the pulsed reactor.

On November 21, 1957, the Scientific Council of the Joint
Institute recommended that a Nuclear Reactions Laboratory
be set up, and Giorgii Flerov, who has pioneered in fission
research, was elected Director of that Laboratory. There is
much evidence that the Joint Institute has been afflicted by
many organizational difficulties. It is true that the installation possesses two gigantic accelerators, the larger of which
had initial operating difficulties. The equipment that services the smaller accelerator is impressive. However, this seems
to be about all the Institute has, and even with the pulsed
reactor it could not pretend to be a well-rounded atomic research center to serve the needs of the Soviet bloc. It is probably roughly a match for the CERN installation at Geneva,
but not nearly as impressive a basic research center as Brookhaven in the United States or Harwell in Britain.

Although the articles of incorporation provide that Joint
Institute officers be elected by majority vote, the Soviets ap-

parently do not place any trust in the situation where a satellite scientist would be a director of one of the laboratories, and apparently the other members are forced to accept this situation. As far as the nonprivileged members are concerned, Dubna may simply represent a drain on their scientific resources, talents, and the limited amount of funds that they can afford to expend for scientific research. This may be precisely what the Soviets have in mind.

The actual costs of the Joint Institute are apportioned as follows: The USSR contributes 47.25 per cent; Communist China, 20 per cent; East Germany and Poland, 6.75 per cent each; Rumania and Czechoslovakia, 5.75 per cent each; Hungary, 4 per cent; Bulgaria, 3.6 per cent; and Albania, North Korea, and Mongolia, a token sum of .05 per cent each. North Vietnam, which is represented on the Scientific Council of the Institute, apparently does not contribute anything. Thus, the USSR is obtaining gratis support for over 50 per cent of its Dubna expenses. The European Organization for Nuclear Research (CERN), which the Joint Institute strives to imitate, has a similar scale of contributions for its Western European members, but the situation is such at CERN that no single nation benefits abnormally with respect to the other members.

Over all, the Joint Institute for Nuclear Research probably represents a bonus for the Soviet Union. The Soviets seem to be willing to risk the possibility that the effectiveness of the Dubna work will be sharply reduced by the organizational squabbles that are bound to occur, by the political instabilities, and by the transient nature of the workers there. The USSR can chance this because it is setting up a complex network of similar cities to which the satellite nations will be denied the privilege of making their contributions.

One city to which frequent reference has been made is, of course, Obninsk, which is the site of the 5,000-kilowatt atomic power station that has been operating since the sum-

mer of 1954. Since that time Obninsk has become an expanding complex of nuclear laboratories of increasing importance to the USSR program. The scientific complex that
has resulted is now known as the Institute of Physics of the
Chief Directorate for the Utilization of Atomic Energy of the
Council of Ministers (Glavatom). A number of experimental
nuclear reactors have since been constructed at this Institute,
among them being a beryllium-moderated reactor and four
or five plutonium-fueled fast reactors. An experimental
mobile 2,000-kilowatt atomic power station is also being
tested at this site. Certainly the associated experimental
apparatus and the chemical and metallurgical facilities required to support the long-range reactor development program of the Institute of Physics of Glavatom must be extensive, and so the new city of Obninsk must be considered a
major atomic center in the USSR.

In view of the extreme difficulty in obtaining information
on the nuclear research and development organizations that
were established in the Stalin period, it is a somewhat more
pleasant task to be able to record the plans for an immense
new scientific center in which atomic energy will play a
dominant role. At various times in the past, there have been
established, under the aegis of the Academy of Sciences of
the USSR, numerous scientific institutes in the vast Siberian
region. Institutes exist at cities such as Irkutsk and Yakutsk,
and more recently a Physics Institute was established at the
city of Krasnoyarsk.

On May 18, 1957, the Council of Ministers of the USSR
resolved to establish a Siberian Section of the Academy of
Sciences of the USSR and, more significantly, to construct an
immense scientific city on the bank of the Ob' River, south
of Novosibirsk. It is evident from the published plans and
from the names of the people associated with the new city
that this community will eventually represent the greatest
and most diversified scientific collective in the world. Indeed,

it will be unique, for it is difficult to name a similar installation anywhere. The new Siberian scientific center not only will provide a major nuclear research installation, but will include important institutes of other sciences that will, to the greatest extent possible, also use nuclear techniques in their research.

Initial construction started in 1958 at the 1,100-hectare (approximately 4¼ square miles) site with a 1958 budget of 290 million rubles, which corresponds roughly to $50 million. Clearly this is an ambitious project. During 1958 first priority was given to the establishment of three institutes at the site.

The Nuclear Physics Institute (sometimes simply referred to as the Physics Institute) will be a branch of Kurchatov's Institute of Atomic Energy at Moscow and will have as its Director Artzimovich's protégé, G. I. Budker. A core of sixty to eighty scientists, mainly young ones, will form the *initial* group. Budker's main interests are in the field of controlled thermonuclear energy problems, and it is the stated task of his new Institute to work on that problem. It will also work on nuclear accelerators using new principles, and undoubtedly Budker's unorthodox (see Chapter 18) ideas along these lines will be tested at the Siberian Institute. Two other institutes had first priority during 1958. The first of these was Academician Mikhail A. Lavrentiev's Hydrodynamics Institute, which, along with its other problems, is charged with investigating underground explosions, a subject of vital importance to the question of clandestine testing of atomic bombs and toward using nuclear explosions for construction purposes. Still unequipped, the hydrodynamics building is the only building that Vice President Nixon was allowed to visit during his "tour" of the new scientific city in July 1959. The other first-priority institute was that of Geology and Geophysics, which will investigate strategic mineral deposits in Siberia. Ten other institutes will be constructed at the site, two of them almost entirely concerned with atomic energy. These two are the Thermophysics Institute and the Inorganic Chemistry Institute. The former institute will be directed by Ivan Ivanovich Novikov, the aforementioned director of the Moscow Engineering Physics Institute. His new institute is specifically charged with problems of developing the use of atomic energy for power purposes. A branch of the Kurnakov Institute of General and Inorganic Chemistry at Moscow—the Institute of Inorganic Chemistry—will be charged with investigating chemical problems involved in the use of atomic energy. Because of this emphasis on nuclear energy and the charge to "conduct bold experiments in atomic physics," it is evident that, if the work of these institutes is to be effective, nuclear reactors and powerful accelerators will be built at the Siberian center.

There are eight other institutes: The Institute of Mathematics and Computing Center will be directed by S. L. Sobolev, a former associate of Kurchatov at Laboratory No. 2. Its task will be to develop computing machines and techniques and to provide computational assistance, including the solution of the complex numerical problems involved in atomic energy. The Institute of Kinetics and Combustion Engineering will work on problems involving very high pressures and extremely high temperatures. The Institute of Automation and Electrometrics will develop new methods of measurement. The Institute of Theoretical and Applied Mechanics will concentrate on two major areas—machine technology and aerodynamics. The Institute of Economics and Statistics will perform tasks in connection with economic problems of Siberia, and will work in conjunction with Sobolev's Institute on computing techniques. An Institute of High Tension Technology is to be established, but its functions have not been specified. The remaining two institutes—the Institute of Cytology and Genetics and the Institute of Experimental Biology and Medicine—will attack biological problems.

It is specified that all of these institutes use isotopic research methods wherever applicable. The city, as yet unnamed, near Novosibirsk, is the forerunner of similar bases (but probably with less of a nuclear slant) to be set up elsewhere. For example, in the period 1958–65, a new scientific city is to be established near Irkutsk. Cities near Krasnoyarsk and Vladivostok are being planned for later development.

In 1956, plans were revealed to construct a new city called "Akademgrad" (for "City of the Academy of Sciences"), "on the picturesque high banks of the Oka not far from Serpukhov and 125 kilometers from Moscow." This description would place the city somewhat south of Serpukhov, about at Aleksin. According to the plans, here there will also be a complex of installations in which radioactive isotope laboratories will be built, though no institute devoted specifically to nuclear research has been mentioned. Eventually, 10,000 people will live in Akademgrad.

Near Alma-Ata a small, 140-million-ruble (approximately $25 million) installation for nuclear physics research will be constructed by 1960. It will be under the control of the Kazakhstan Academy of Sciences. As is the case in the other scientific cities, workers will be housed on the site, which will be approximately two square miles in area. Servicing the 15 small laboratories of the Institute will be a nuclear research reactor and a cyclotron.

Clearly, there are many reasons underlying the establishment of the new cities. Right after the war, because convenient contact was necessary for obtaining required instrumentation and technical equipment immediately, it was necessary to carry out the bulk of atomic energy development work in areas having an initially large concentration of scientific and industrial resources, mainly at Moscow and

Leningrad. It was also necessary to train vast numbers of young technicians and scientists at locales where qualified instructors and equipment were available. For an entire decade the newly trained scientists and newly constructed research equipment were increasingly concentrated at a few locations. The net effect of this is that the Moscow area, particularly, is bursting at its seams with scientific laboratories, scientists, and technicians.

Thus there is the problem of actual accommodation in Moscow. Also, the scientists are reluctant to forgo the amenities of a large city and are not eager to staff the industrial complexes that have sprung up throughout the USSR. Of course, this situation is also true for many of the nonnuclear sciences and technologies.

Moreover, the concentration of huge scientific technical forces at a few cities creates a strategically vulnerable situation, for if Moscow, Leningrad, and Kharkov were to be destroyed today, there is no question that the bulk of Russia's scientific resources would be wiped out, and the road toward recovery of scientific and technical self-sufficiency would be very long.

Thus eventually the USSR will literally be peppered with unique scientific communities, a phenomenon that almost constitutes a new social concept. However, the philosophy is not far different from that which has caused the Soviet Union in the past to establish other types of collectives—industrial and agricultural. Each of the scientific cities is to work on regional problems, but the given tasks of the nuclear installations at the Novosibirsk scientific city and the others transcend any regional problems.

Will the underlying collective aura of the new cities stifle the scientific talents within them, or will the long-range effect be as beneficial as Soviet planners hope? Here is an entirely new pattern that the West cannot ignore.

18

ATTACK ON THE FUTURE

The most costly, and perhaps the most impressive, of the physicists' tools are the machines that accelerate elementary atomic particles to exceedingly high energies—energies at which the most complex nuclear particles can be made to disintegrate and, indeed, entirely new strange particles begin to appear. A prominent physicist was once asked by an administrator to justify the costs of a gigantic accelerator he was about to build. He was asked in particular what he expected to find after the machine had been constructed. The physicist replied that if he knew what he expected to find he would have no use for the machine in the first place. Thus the accelerator is the physicists' tool for probing into the unknown. And since this probing on a nuclear scale is extremely forceful, in a sense the accelerating machines can be considered the physicists' artillery.

For the most advanced of these machines that produce energies of cosmic magnitudes there are few, if any, foresee-

able practical applications; yet in the post–World War II
period, the construction of these machines has received unprecedented financial support from many governments.
Indeed, the USSR not only is not an exception but has
achieved some spectacular successes that they now exploit
in the form of a sputnik or a lunik.

There is now in the USSR such a profusion of small and
large nuclear accelerating machines in use in scientific institutes and in factory laboratories that a complete listing of
the accelerators would be a major project in itself and would
probably serve no useful purpose except to show the extent
of the Soviet accelerator program. This is already evident
from general considerations. It will, perhaps, suffice therefore to list here a few of the major accelerator developments.
In doing so, it will be necessary to define only too briefly
some of the different types of accelerating machines that will
be encountered. Some of the labels are peculiar to Soviet
literature, so their Western equivalents will also be given.
The Soviet scientists themselves are beginning to use the
terms interchangeably.

The basic types of accelerators for obtaining high-energy
nuclear particles are as follows:

The *linear accelerator,* by a suitable combination of electric and/or magnetic fields, progressively accelerates particles
down a long tube. This is the earliest type of accelerator
developed, and several variants of it, producing particles of
low energy, are to be found in various USSR laboratories.
At the Kharkov Physico-Technical Institute, a group under
the direction of K. D. Sinel'nikov[1] specializes in designing
linear accelerators for use as beam injectors for the larger
accelerating machines. Most of the significant USSR accelerators, however, are of the circular type and fall into the
other categories.

The *cyclotron* was invented and developed by the late
Ernest O. Lawrence at the University of California in the

early 1930's. It will be recalled that the first cyclotron in Europe was constructed in the USSR by Kurchatov and his collaborators, and a number have since been built in the USSR. However, there are definite limits to the energies that can be obtained in a cyclotron and it was therefore necessary to devise new principles to accelerate particles to higher energies. These principles essentially consist in providing certain types of variations of electric and magnetic fields. The variations are complex and will not be elaborated upon here, but a few of the different types of machines will be listed.

The next complex elaboration of the cyclotron is the *synchrotron,* which accelerates electrons. It represents the first step forward in obtaining higher energies. The principle of the synchrotron was discovered by a Russian, Vladimir I. Veksler, and it was communicated and published in a Russian journal as early as April 1944. This was at the time when some Soviet physicists had just resumed their work, so this must have represented one of the earlier fruits of Veksler's renewed labor. Subsequently, an American, Dr. Edwin McMillan, a colleague of Lawrence's, independently discovered the same principle in July 1945. McMillan's work was published in September 1945, but Veksler protested and claimed earlier priority. McMillan gracefully acknowledged in a later letter that "it is clear that Veksler's discovery of the principle was earlier." Veksler stated in his letter of protest that a 30-Mev machine using his principle was nearing completion at the Lebedev Physics Institute of the Academy of Sciences of the USSR, and it would seem that this was the first high-energy electron accelerator to be built in the USSR in the postwar period. Later, in 1948, a machine with an energy rating ten times that of Veksler's came into operation at the University of California, but the Soviets were not far behind. In the last days of 1949, also at the Lebedev Institute, a machine of approximately the same size as the American one went into operation. The 30-Mev and 280-Mev machines are still being usefully employed at the Institute for advanced research.

It is pertinent to note the time at which this larger machine went into operation, for it corresponds roughly to the achievement of the first Soviet atomic bomb. It therefore represents a diversion of men and materials during a period when such were scarce and the atomic bomb had highest development priority. And the decision to proceed with a large accelerator construction program must have been made in 1947, concurrently with the vital decision on the atomic bomb. But, more significantly, the Veksler accelerator was neither the largest nor the most expensive one to be put into operation during this critical period. This honor belongs to the gigantic *phasotron* (which in U.S. terminology would be called a "synchrocyclotron") at a then highly secret laboratory some 60 miles north of Moscow, at Dubna. The construction of this phasotron, as might be supposed, was one of the multiple responsibilties of Igor Kurchatov, and "it is to him that much of the credit for its ultimate success is due." Coming into operation on December 14, 1949, the phasotron was designed to accelerate protons, much heavier particles than electrons, to energies of 280 Mev, and alpha particles to energies of 560 Mev. At the end of 1950 the phasotron was converted to accelerate protons to energies of about 500 Mev, and in 1953, after an extensive nuclear research program with the various particles of the above energies, the machine was converted to give proton energies of 680 Mev. This is indeed an impressive machine and is so arranged that as many as 12 to 16 different experiments can be carried out simultaneously on it. As Dr. Luis Alvarez, another colleague of Lawrence's, described it, "I have seen all the large American cyclotrons, and this is better engineered than any of ours."[2]

The modest manner in which the Dubna phasotron first came to the attention of the Western world is rather curious. The first papers giving results of experiments done on the machines were submitted to a Russian journal in November 1954 and published in December. Western scientists did not become fully aware of the implications of those papers until March 1955. It should be recalled that during the Stalin period and for approximately a year afterward, all Soviet nuclear science, whether pure or applied, was classified. There is therefore no reason why the Russian phasotron work that was performed up to 1953 would have been declassified at that time. After the phasotron was reconstructed to provide particles of higher energy, Soviet scientists probably preferred to publish newer work with a machine of increased capacity, so that, allowing time for further experimentation and analysis, the actual publication date at the end of 1954 appears to be explainable.

Until the middle of 1956 the Dubna phasotron was the largest *of its type* in the world. However, since the operation of the University of California machine at energies in excess of 700 Mev, the Dubna installation has had to take second place. But the Soviets have been working on still more powerful accelerating machines of different types.

A synchrophasotron that operates on still different principles and is capable of producing exceedingly energetic nuclear particles came into operation during March 1957. When it did so, it took the lead from two similar U.S. machines: the 2-Bev *cosmotron* at Brookhaven National Laboratory and the 6.2-Bev *bevatron* at the University of California Radiation Laboratory. Proton beam energies of 10 Bev were obtained in the new Russian synchrophasotron in May 1957; this represented the greatest energy ever attained in a nuclear machine. In size, the 10-Bev machine is most impressive, for the weight of its magnet alone is 36,000 tons

(the weight of a heavy cruiser), and the diameter of the
device is about 200 feet. The estimated equivalent U.S. cost
for such a machine would be about $100 million. There
appear to have been a number of difficulties in getting the
device to operate properly, and many of the Russian scientists themselves felt that it was rushed into premature operation mainly for prestige purposes. But by 1958 the difficulties appear to have been removed and the machine apparently is now the high-caliber research machine that they
claim it to be. In April 1959 its designers and constructers
received the coveted Lenin prize.

The physical location of the 10-Bev synchrophasotron is
at the Electro-Physical Institute directed by Veksler and is
part of the Dubna research complex that now is called the
Joint Institute for Nuclear Research. (Veksler's Institute is
now officially termed the High Energy Laboratory of the
Joint Institute.) In the international race for machines of
higher energy, the Dubna device will be outstripped, about
1960, by a machine being built at Brookhaven and by one at
the European Organization for Nuclear Research (CERN)
at Geneva. These Western machines will be in the range of
from 25 to 30 Bev. However, the Russians do not like to be
left behind, and at the Institute of Electro-Physical Apparatus (apparently the major accelerator engineering design
organization in the USSR) at Leningrad, a 50-Bev synchrophasotron is in a late planning stage. Using new principles,
the new machine will weigh less than the 10-Bev machine,
that is, approximately 22,000 tons. It will, however, have an
impressively large diameter of over 1,500 feet. The location
of the 50-Bev machine is not known, and because it definitely
does not seem to be called for in the published advance plans
of the Joint Institute for Nuclear Research, it seems likely
that it will not be at Dubna. Moreover, the theoretical aspects are under the direction of V. V. Vladimirskii, who is

not usually identified with Veksler's group but with A. I. Alikhanov's Thermotechnical Laboratory. Undoubtedly, after this 50-Bev machine is built, the Russians will again temporarily lose their lead to a Western machine. However, it is certain that they will bid higher and higher, and Veksler himself in 1955 gave some indication of how high their final bid might be: "I do not doubt, however, that experimental physics will succeed in solving this problem too, and that we shall learn how to create artificially particles with enormous energies of the order of a million million to ten million million electron-volts."[3]

At international meetings held in Russia in May 1956 and in Geneva in June 1956, Soviet scientists gave some indication of how they are going to attempt to reach these higher energies and to improve accelerator designs. Veksler described the concept of making the accelerating field appear only in the vicinity of the accelerated particle itself. This is a very advanced relativistic concept, and the reader should not be bothered if it is not clear to him, for at least one of the prominent U.S. accelerator experts present at Veksler's talk has confessed an inability to understand the concept. Another, even more speculative, idea was presented by G. I. Budker, who described the possibility of using the so-called pinch effect, which is important in thermonuclear work, to provide in accelerators of very small diameters intense proton beams having energies as high as 100 Bev. A very-small-scale model has already been built. If Budker's large-scale machine can actually be realized, then the energies obtained will be a tenth of the way toward Veksler's envisioned goal.

19

HARNESSING THE STARS

It is quite clear that if Nikolai Bukharin's 1927 offer of the entire electrical output of the city of Leningrad for research in the production of thermonuclear energy had been accepted by the scientists, it would have been to no avail. But the story illustrates the willingness of Soviet planners to venture into untried fields, then and now. For in the 1920's, the knowledge required to simulate the types of nuclear reactions that occur in our sun and other stars was entirely inadequate and undeveloped. Much of the required information came to light during the 1930's, which, to the world over, represents a period of remarkable discoveries in the field of nuclear physics, particularly at the Cavendish Laboratory in England and at the Enrico Fermi Laboratory at Rome. Almost all of the experiments on the nuclear physics of light elements, which were to prove so important later, were immediately repeated and extended in the laboratory of Igor V. Kurchatov as soon as they had been performed outside of Russia. It is thus not unnatural that after the Soviet physicists had accomplished their primary mission of achieving the atomic bomb they should turn to research on a promising new energy source, and the year 1950 appears to be the date when Soviet research on controlled thermo-nuclear reactions was started. This is approximately one to two years before similar work was initiated on a serious scale in Britain and the United States.

As the name "thermonuclear" implies, the problem in-volved is to heat an appropriate isotope, such as deuterium (a heavy isotope of hydrogen), to a temperature so high that the deuterium nuclei, by virtue of their thermal motions alone, will collide, combine, and thus emit large quantities of energy. If the emitted energy can be used for the further heating of gas, the reaction will be self-sustaining. As Kurcha-tov has pointed out, the amount of energy required to heat such a gas initially "is about the same amount of energy required to boil water in the family samovar." The problem involved, however, is to transfer all of this energy to the deuterium nuclei and to prevent it from radiating out again into space. The major approaches to this heat-containment problem are remarkably similar in the U.S., the USSR, and Britain. The first opportunity to make such a comparison occurred when some of the Soviet experiments were described at the British Nuclear Research Establishment at Harwell on April 25, 1956, by Kurchatov, who had accompanied Khru-shchev on his visit to Britain.

Both the United States and the Soviet Union—the latter perhaps a bit earlier—were able to produce "spurious" ther-monuclear reactions in their apparatus, and by very interest-ing diagnostic and theoretical work were able to recognize independently the spurious reactions as such. The British and U.S. work was announced simultaneously on January 24, 1958; and on January 29 a Soviet broadcast hailed the British work and depreciated that of the United States simply by not mentioning it. On February 28, Academician Kurchatov drove the wedge still further by giving a fuller description of the British work and stating that the American work basically did not represent any new facts. Within six months after the specifications for the British thermonuclear machine "Zeta" had been released, the Russians had completed in Leningrad a faithful reproduction named "Alpha." This can be taken as an indication that the Soviet thermonuclear program was still seeking direction and that all possibilities were being considered and tried. Incidentally, the British have abandoned their "Zeta" work, since that direction appears unpromising.

What is perhaps more interesting than the relative technical progress of the three countries in the thermonuclear field is the fact that the Soviets have recognized the emotional and political appeal of a development of such promise. There are strong indications that the Soviets may feel that the momentary political value of their work may be more important than the possible future end results. And in this respect, Igor Kurchatov represents the political, as well as the technical, instrument for implementing the Soviet-controlled thermonuclear reaction program.

Because it was believed that controlled thermonuclear reactions might possibly have military implications, the programs of the various nations engaged in this field were classified until the spring of 1956. It was Igor Kurchatov and his Harwell talk that broke the classification barrier for the first time. The world reaction to his talk was more than he possibly could have expected, and the Soviet press and radio were quick to follow this coup with self-praise. In 1956 Kurchatov also made an offer to the scientists of the world to the effect that if they could persuade their governments to agree to a ban on the use of nuclear weapons, the Soviet scientists could cooperate in thermonuclear research with their Western colleagues, which would open the way for full scientific cooperation among all nations of the world. Two years later Kurchatov re-emphasized this issue. He pointed out that eminent American physicists, such as Edward Teller, who were closely connected with the hydrogen bomb, were also working on the peaceful controlled thermonuclear reactions; he also emphasized the possible military applications of controlled thermonuclear reactions. Kurchatov concluded that in this atmosphere it would be impossible to expect complete frankness among scientists of different nations and concluded again that complete cooperation was possible only if nuclear weapons were banned. Professor Kurchatov's excessive modesty in neglecting to mention his own dominant role in the development and production of nuclear weapons is perhaps commendable, if not frank.

On the technical level, the controlled thermonuclear work is the responsibility of Kurchatov's Institute of Atomic Energy in Moscow, and, to a lesser extent, of Moscow State University, and of institutes in Sukhumi, Leningrad, and Kharkov. A special thermonuclear section is headed by Academician Lev Andreevich Artzimovich, whose background marks him as an expert in the fields of electron optics and atomic accelerators. Both of these related arts are important in the controlling of thermonuclear reactions. Also, as was the case in the United States, many persons engaged in the thermonuclear effort were recruited from the cadres that earlier worked on the electromagnetic separation of isotopes. Artzimovich played an essential role—perhaps the leading one— in the latter effort. A deputy director of the Institute, I. N. Golovin, is credited with the development of some of the larger thermonuclear research apparatus. The theoretical thermonuclear work is directed by Academician M. A. Leontovich, assisted by a number of able young theoreticians, in-

cluding Academicians A. D. Sakharov, V. D. Shafronov, and
G. I. Budker. In June 1956, at a meeting held in Geneva,
young Budker impressed his Western colleagues by describing an imaginative and revolutionary type of nuclear accelerator (described in Chapter 18) that could have important
application in the thermonuclear problem. Rewarded for
his outstanding work, Budker has recently been sent to head
the newly established Institute of Physics of the great scientific complex being established near Novosibirsk in Siberia.
Budker's institute will act as an extension of Artzimovich's
laboratory, so it should become one of the two most important centers of thermonuclear research in the USSR.

In August 1958, Chinese scientists at the Institute of
Atomic Energy in Peking were treated to a preview description of an experimental thermonuclear device (named
"Ogra") that had just been built at the Moscow IAE.
Resembling a wind tunnel 65 feet long and 4½ feet in diameter, Ogra dwarfed any thermonuclear device in the West.
It has certain similarities to another, smaller device known
as "DCX," developed at the Oak Ridge National Laboratories. At the 1958 Geneva Conference on the Peaceful Uses
of Atomic Energy, the United States and Britain formally
lifted all secrecy on data that will be obtained from DCX
and all other controlled thermonuclear experimentation. It
is to be hoped that as data are obtained, Ogra (honoring, in
reverse fashion, *A*rtzimovich-*G*olovin, but also representing
the basic root for the Russian words denoting "guarded" or
"restricted") and its kin will be discussed just as freely by
Soviet scientists.

Artzimovich and several of his colleagues have already
been honored with the 1958 Lenin prize for their thermonuclear research. The controlled thermonuclear problem is
still far from solution, however, and it is meaningless at this

point to attribute a "lead" to any one nation. But with its extensive program, at least as large as that of the United States and several times that of Britain, the Soviet Union stands a very good chance of establishing further thermonuclear guideposts of political and technical significance. Thermonuclear energy was the main theme of Kurchatov's speech at the January 1959 Party Congress, at which he spoke of the "enormous attention of the Party Central Committee" and of Comrade Khrushchev personally. Before the same delegates, Mikhail Lavrentiev, Vice President of the Academy of Sciences of the USSR and Chairman of the newly created Siberian section, heavily underscored the importance of the thermonuclear problem and Kurchatov's dominant position in the nuclear program:

The first problem listed by N. S. Khrushchev as facing science in the Seven-Year Plan is controlled thermonuclear reaction. All institutes of the Siberian section—the mathematical, physical, and chemical—will strive to make their contribution to this important task. Any request regarding this problem which we receive from I. V. Kurchatov will be given priority.[1]

As a specific and primary goal of the new Seven-Year Plan, it may be expected that the tempo of thermonuclear research in the Soviet Union will continue to increase.

Kurchatov, among others, has noted that the earth's deposits of uranium and thorium would be sufficient to last only several hundred years if all of the world's power were made dependent on the fission process. This may be an underestimate but, whether the fission time scale is in terms of hundreds or thousands of years, there is sufficient deuterium present in the earth's oceans to meet the world's power requirements, at the present rate of consumption, for about one hundred million million years. Clearly, there is an incentive here for the Soviet Union, as well as for any other

nation, to be the first to tap this enormous resource. As
Francis William Aston, pioneer researcher on isotopes, wrote
in 1926:

How long it will be before man can release and control this
energy, and to what uses he will put such vast potentialities,
are subjects for the philosopher. . . . It may be that the
operation, once started, is uncontrollable and that the new
stars which flare out from time to time are but the notifi-
cation of successful large-scale experiments on far distant
worlds. It may be that the highest form of life on our planet
will one day discover supreme material power, or cataclysmic
annihilation, in the same ocean wherein, we are told, its
lowest forms originally evolved.[2]

NOTES

*See Bibliography for full titles
and publication data.*

CHAPTER ONE: THE ATOM AWAKENED

1. In Russian history, the status of scientist, poet, and statesman Lomonosov is somewhat equivalent to that of his contemporary, Benjamin Franklin, in the United States.

2. H. G. Wells, *The World Set Free: A Story of Mankind,* New York, 1914, p. 117.

3. "Essays and Speeches," Petrograd, 1922. Quoted in *Bol'shaia Sovetskaia Entsiklopediia (Great Soviet Encyclopedia),* Vol. 7, p. 500.

4. *Ibid.,* p. 502.

5. A. F. Ioffe, "Can Science Be Planned?" *Moscow News,* June 16, 1945, p. 3.

6. A. S. Eve, *Rutherford,* p. 374.

7. S. I. Vavilov (ed.), editorial introduction to *The Journal of Physics* (USSR), Vol. 1, No. 1, 1939.

CHAPTER TWO: THE EARLY SCIENTIFIC BASE

1. *The Journal of Physics* (USSR), Vol. 3, No. 4-5, 1940, p. 225.

2. This figure is a very rough calculation derived from an estimate of the 1945 costs of somewhat comparable machines made by A. H. Snell ("Reactors or Other Nuclear Machines?" in *Physics Today,* Vol. 7, No. 9, pp. 7-9). The costs have been adjusted to comparable 1939 prices by assuming a 36 per cent increase between 1939 and 1945.

3. The total allocation for capital investment in the Academy of Sciences budget for the year 1941 was 25 million rubles. Assuming a ruble-dollar ratio of 10 to 1 (a reasonable figure in view of the high relative cost of precision laboratory equipment in the USSR), the construction of one cyclotron would have consumed a very large portion of the Academy's budget for capital construction.

4. Manhattan District Reports CP-2630, issued February 8, 1945, and CP-3021, issued June 5, 1945. Originally issued as "Secret," these have since been declassified.

CHAPTER THREE: THE WAR CALLS A HALT

1. Great Britain's effort, of course, was transferred to North America because of the pressures of the war.

2. Ioffe, "Report to the Presidium of the Academy of Sciences of the USSR on the Activities of the Leningrad Physico-Technical Institute, October 2, 1941," *Vestnik Akademii Nauk SSSR (Herald of the Academy of Sciences of the USSR)*, Vol. 11, No. 9-10, p. 67.

3. Ioffe, "Twenty-five Years' Growth of Exact Science in the USSR," *Iubileinaia Sessiia Akademii Nauk SSSR . . . 15–18 noyabria 1942 goda (Jubilee Session of the Academy of Sciences of the USSR . . . November 15–18, 1942)*, Izd-vo Akademii Nauk SSSR, 1943.

4. *Essential Information on Atomic Energy*, prepared by the Special Committee on Atomic Energy, U.S. Senate, pursuant to S. Res. 179, 2d Session, 79th Cong. (Committee Monograph No. 1), Washington, D.C., 1946, p. 31.

5. H. D. Smyth, *A General Account of the Development of Methods of Using Atomic Energy for Military Purposes*, para. 3.15.

CHAPTER FOUR: MOTIVATION

1. No evidence has come to light that Soviet espionage agents were reporting as early as the summer of 1941 (when the Russians abandoned their research program) about atomic matters in the United States and the United Kingdom. Of the agents who were later apprehended, Fuchs began his espionage work earliest, and he did not begin reporting until 1942.

2. *Pravda* and *Izvestiia*, October 13, 1941.

3. P. L. Kapitsa, "Science and War," partially reported in *The New York Times*, March 1, 1942, p. 19, col. 2. Typewritten text available in the Library of Congress. Original in *Krasnaia Zvezda*, February 26, 1942.

CHAPTER FIVE: THE DORMANT PERIOD

1. Kapitsa, "Report on the Organization of Scientific Work of the Institute of Physical Problems of the Academy of Sciences of the USSR," *Vestnik Akademii*, Vol. 13, No. 6, pp. 75–89.

2. *Nature*, August 16, 1947, p. 211.

3. S. A. Goudsmit, *Alsos*, p. 106.

4. See also Goudsmit's testimony before the Special Senate Committee on Atomic Energy, *Hearings* . . . , 79th Congress, 1st Session [on] S. Res. 179, Part 1, p. 264.

5. A. Dulles, *Germany's Underground.*

6. O. Heilbrunn, *The Soviet Secret Services.*

7. Smyth, para. 4.51.

8. Ioffe, "Twenty-five Years' Growth of Exact Science in the USSR," *Iubileinaia Sessiia Akademii Nauk SSSR* . . . , p. 182.

CHAPTER SIX: KEEPING INFORMED

1. V. Kravchenko, *I Chose Freedom*, pp. 426–27.

2. "Report Concerning the Disappearance of Two Former Foreign Office Officials," British White Paper, September 23, 1955. See also *The London Times*, September 24, 1955, pp. 4, 6–7.

3. W. L. White, "Secret from Whom?" *The Reader's Digest*, March 1950, p. 65.

4. J. Stalin, "Dialectical and Historical Materialism," *Voprosy Leninizma (Problems of Leninism)*, p. 325.

5. W. D. Leahy, *I Was There*, p. 265.

6. *Ibid.*, pp. 440–42.

7. E. R. Stettinius, Jr., *Roosevelt and the Russians*, p. 90.

8. *Foreign Relations of the United States: Diplomatic Papers—The Conferences at Malta and Yalta, 1945*, pp. 357–58.

CHAPTER SEVEN: HIROSHIMA AND THE KREMLIN

1. Y. Delbar, *The Real Stalin.*

2. J. R. Deane, *The Strange Alliance.*

3. W. S. Churchill, *The Second World War*, Vol. V: *Closing the Ring*, p. 375.

4. Churchill, *ibid.*, Vol. VI: *Triumph and Tragedy*, p. 641.

5. A highly readable personal account of the U.S. Manhattan Project, A. H. Compton's *Atomic Quest* describes these circumstances in greater detail.

6. Another chronological analysis is A. K. Smith's "Behind the Decision To Use the Atomic Bomb: Chicago, 1944–45," *Bulletin of the Atomic Scientists*, October 1958.

7. M. Amrine, *The Great Decision*, discusses the same theme.

8. D. D. Eisenhower, *Crusade in Europe.*

9. Detailed analyses and discussion of the Japanese surrender decision are found in T. Kase, *Journey to the Missouri.*

10. R. J. C. Butow, *Japan's Decision To Surrender.*

11. *The New York Times*, October 9, 1945.

12. H. S. Truman, *Years of Decision*, p. 423.

13. *The New York Times,* August 10, 1945.
14. "Soviet Atomic Espionage" [testimony of Harry Gold], Joint Committee on Atomic Energy, p. 157.
15. *U.S. Congress Hearings on Senate Resolution No. 179.*
16. Personal communication from Mr. Mikolajczyk to M. J. Ruggles, March 1956.
17. Eisenhower, *Crusade in Europe.*
18. M. Rubinstein, "The Foreign Press on the Atomic Bomb," *New Times,* No. 7, September 1, 1945, pp. 12–17.
19. *Literaturnaya Gazeta (Literary Gazette),* No. 46 (1157), November 7, 1945.
20. J. F. Byrnes, *Speaking Frankly.*
21. *Soviet News,* No. 1235, August 21, 1945, p. 3.
22. *The New York Times,* August 10, 1945.

CHAPTER EIGHT: THE SCIENTISTS RENEW THEIR EFFORTS

1. A. Baikov, "General Orientation of the Plan of Work of the Academy of Sciences of the USSR for 1944," *Obshchee Sobranie Akademii Nauk SSSR,* September 25-30, 1943.
2. Y. I. Frenkel, "Problems of Contemporary Physics," *Vestnik Akademii Nauk,* Vol. 4-5, 1943, p. 100.
3. *Ibid.,* p .108.
4. Kapitsa, "The Organization of Scientific Work in the Institute for Physical Problems of the Academy of Sciences of the USSR," *Vestnik Akademii Nauk,* Vol. 6, 1943.
5. *Les Sciences Naturelles en URSS depuis 25 ans,* Moscow, 1943.
6. *Vestnik Akademii Nauk,* Vol. 4-5, 1943, p. 100.

CHAPTER NINE: THEIR FIRST CHAIN REACTION

1. "Abstracts of Reports Presented at the Nuclear Physics Conference," *Journal of Physics of the USSR,* Vol. 4, No. 3, 1941, pp. 277–86.
2. G. A. Tokaev, *Soviet Imperialism.*
3. "Materials of Conference on the Physics of Atomic Nuclei," *Bulletin de l'Academie des Sciences de l'URSS, Série Physique,* 11/26/40, Vol. 5, 1941, pp. 555–87.
4. Speech before the American-Russian Institute on May 19, 1947, *The New York Times,* May 20, 1947.
5. V. S. Fursov, "Works of the USSR Academy of Sciences on Uranium-Graphite Reactors," Session of the Academy of Sciences of the USSR on Peaceful Utilization of Atomic Energy, July 1-5, 1955, pp. 15-38.
6. L. D. Landau, "The Atom of Uranium—A New Source of Energy," *Ogonek,* No. 35, 1945, published August 25, 1945, p. 14.

7. Byrnes, *Speaking Frankly.*
8. Fursov, "Works . . . on Uranium-Graphite Reactors."

CHAPTER TEN: THE BOMB

1. *The New York Times,* September 26, 1949.
2. The White House statement by the President for release in the morning papers, October 24, 1956.
3. *Pravda* and *Izvestiia,* August 9, 1953.
4. TASS announcement, *Pravda* and *Izvestiia,* August 20, 1953.
5. *Pravda,* November 28, 1955.
6. *The New York Times,* April 1, 1954, p. 20.
7. *Pravda,* March 15, 1958.
8. Broadcast by Soviet Home Service, February 5, 1959.

CHAPTER ELEVEN: THE GENERAL'S PLOWSHARES

1. Y. A. Dolmatovskii, "Your Strength," *Novy Mir,* July 1949, p. 170.
2. *Pravda* and *Izvestiia,* September 26, 1949.
3. *Pravda,* May 11, 1957.
4. A. Goncharenko, "At the Central Seismic Station Instruments Register Nuclear Explosions," *Krasnaia Zvezda,* September 23, 1956, p. 2.
5. *Pravda,* April 1, 1958.

CHAPTER TWELVE: "OUR ATOM OF PEACE"

1. *Trud,* July 4, 1954, p. 2.
2. *Soviet News,* August 14, 1959.
3. *Pravda,* August 14, 1959.

CHAPTER THIRTEEN: THE MOBILE ATOM

1. Recently the capacity of this reactor has been raised from 300 kilowatts to 3,000 kilowatts.
2. Report of the Underseas Warfare Advisory Panel, Joint Committee on Atomic Energy.
3. *Voyennaya Mysl',* No. 9, September 1955, p. 30.
4. *Ibid.,* p. 6.
5. *Financial Times,* London, May 19, 1959, p. 8.
6. *The New York Times,* July 28, 1959, p. 11.
7. *Twentieth Session of the Communist Party of the Soviet Union,* Vol. 2, p. 437.

CHAPTER FIFTEEN: MATERIAL RESOURCES

1. Staromonetny Lane No. 35, in south Moscow.

CHAPTER SIXTEEN: THE ORGANIZATION AND THE INSTITUTES

1. Kravchenko, *I Chose Freedom.*
2. In Moscow guidebooks, the addresses of all Ministries save the Ministry of Medium Machine Building and the Ministry of Defense Industries are given. However, if the reader is moved to make further inquiries of the former, he may request the Moscow operator to ring K5-28-13.

CHAPTER EIGHTEEN: ATTACK ON THE FUTURE

1. The versatile Sinel'nikov also directs programs in thermonuclear research and in special alloys for nuclear reactors.
2. L. W. Alvarez, "Excerpts from a Russian Diary," *Physics Today*, May 1957, p. 30.
3. Lecture by V. I. Veksler, "Principles of Acceleration of Charged Particles," Geneva, August 1955. Also in *Atomnaya Energiya*, No. 1, Moscow, 1956, pp. 75–82.

CHAPTER NINETEEN: HARNESSING THE STARS

1. *Pravda*, February 1, 1959.
2. F. W. Aston, *Encyclopaedia Britannica*, 13th ed. (1926), Vol. 1, p. 267.

BIBLIOGRAPHY

Despite the extremely strict secrecy that surrounds Soviet technical developments, there exists in the stacks of the U.S. Library of Congress and other libraries a veritable treasure house of information for the serious and patient student of Soviet science. In the correlation and resolution of the various scraps of information he will find but a small fraction of the answers he seeks; but, in view of the fact that even those few answers cannot be obtained simply and directly from the Soviet Union, at least some satisfaction may be derived from the achievement of this minimal knowledge. The present study has by no means exhausted all of the information sources available. A number of the more important quotations and sources have been referenced in the text. Some of the more important general sources are:

Acta Physico-Chimica URSS. Moscow.

All-Union Conference on the Application of Radioactive and Stable Isotopes and Radiation in the National Economy and Science, Moscow, April 2–5, 1957 (abstracts).

Amrine, M. The Great Decision. New York, Putnam, 1959.

Armand, A. A. (ed.). The Scientific Research Institutes of

Heavy Industry. Leningrad, 1935. Armand was at the time director of the Scientific Research Sector of the People's Commissariat of Heavy Industry. This 1028-page volume is a comprehensive handbook on virtually all Soviet scientific research institutes in the mid-1930's.

Atomnaya Energiya, Moscow.

Bardin, I. P. Stalin and Soviet Metallurgy. Moscow, Foreign Languages Publishing House, 1951.

Bogdanov, A. Krasnaia Zvezda (Red Star). Moscow, Knigoizdatel'stvo pisatelei, 1918.

Bol'shaia Sovetskaia Entsiklopediia (Great Soviet Encyclopedia). 2d ed. Moscow, 1950–58.

Borodin, N. M. One Man in His Time. New York, The Macmillan Company, 1955.

British White Paper, "Report Concerning the Disappearance of Two Former Foreign Office Officials." London, September 23, 1955.

Bukharin, N. I. "Theory and Practice from the Standpoint of Dialectical Materialism," in Science at the Crossroads. London, Kniga, Ltd., 1931. (Science at the Crossroads is a collection of USSR contributions to the International Congress of the History of Science and Technology held in London, June 20 to July 3, 1931.)

Bulletin de l'Académie des Sciences de l'URSS, Série Physique (Bulletin of the Academy of Sciences of the USSR, Physics Series). Moscow.

Bulletin of the Atomic Scientists, Vol. 1, No. 10. Chicago, May 1, 1946.

Butow, R. J. C. Japan's Decision to Surrender. Stanford, Stanford University Press, 1954.

Byrnes, J. F. Speaking Frankly. New York, Harper & Brothers, 1947.

Churchill, W. S. The Second World War. Vol. IV, The Hinge of Fate; Vol. V, Closing the Ring; Vol. VI, Triumph and Tragedy. Boston, Houghton Mifflin Co., 1950, 1951, 1953.

Comptes-Rendus de l'Académie des Sciences de l'URSS (Proceedings of the Academy of Sciences of the USSR). Moscow.

Compton, A. H. Atomic Quest. New York, Oxford University Press, 1956.

Craven, W. F., and Cate, J. L. (eds.). The Army Air Forces in World War II, Vol. 5. Chicago, University of Chicago Press, 1953.

Crowther, J. G. Soviet Science. New York, E. P. Dutton & Co., 1936.

Deane, J. R. The Strange Alliance. New York, The Viking Press, 1947.

Delbar, Y. The Real Stalin. Translated from the French by Bernard Miall. London, George Allen and Unwin, Ltd., 1953.

Dinerstein, Herbert S. War and the Soviet Union: Nuclear Weapons and the Revolution in Soviet Military and Political Thinking. New York, Frederick A. Praeger, Inc., 1959.

Dulles, A. Germany's Underground. New York, The Macmillan Company, 1947.

Eisenhower, D. D. Crusade in Europe. Garden City, N.Y., Doubleday & Co., Inc., 1948.

"Essential Information on Atomic Energy" prepared by Special Committee on Atomic Energy pursuant to S. Res. 179, 2d Session, 79th Congress, Committee Monograph No. 1, Washington, D.C., 1946.

Eve, A. S. Rutherford. Cambridge, England, Cambridge University Press, 1939.

Fersman, A. Y. Les Sciences naturelles en URSS depuis 25 ans (The Natural Sciences in the USSR During the Last 25 Years.) Editions en langues étrangères. Moscow, 1943.

Foreign Relations of the United States: Diplomatic Papers— The Conferences at Malta and Yalta, 1945. Washington, D.C., U.S. Government Printing Office, 1955.

Frolov, Y. S. et al. "Development of Isotope Production in the USSR," Moscow, 1957 (pamphlet). Available as U.S. Atomic Energy Commission Translation No. 3093.

Garthoff, R. L. Soviet Military Doctrine. Glencoe, Ill. The Free Press, 1953.

———. Soviet Strategy in the Nuclear Age. New York, Frederick A. Praeger, Inc., 1958.

Goudsmit, S. A. Alsos. New York, Schuman, 1947.

Heilbrunn, O. The Soviet Secret Services. New York, Frederick A. Praeger, Inc., 1956.

International Affairs, Moscow.

Ioffe, A. F. "Physics and Technology," in Science at the Crossroads. London, Kniga, Ltd., 1931.

——. Nekotorye problemy sovremennoi fiziki (Several Problems of Contemporary Physics). Moscow, Ogiz sotsekgiz, 1941.

Iubileinaia Sessiia Akademii Nauk SSSR . . . 15–18 noyabria 1942 goda (Jubilee Session of the Academy of Sciences of the USSR . . . November 15–18, 1942). Moscow, Izd-vo Akademii Nauk SSSR, 1943.

Izvestiia, Moscow.

Izvestiia Akademii Nauk SSSR, Ser. Fiz. (News of the Academy of Sciences of the USSR, Physics Series), Moscow.

The Journal of Physics (USSR), Moscow.

Kase, T. Journey to the Missouri. New Haven, Conn., Yale University Press, 1950.

Kol'man, E. Noveishie Otkrytiia Sovremennoi Atomnoi Fiziki v Svete Dialekticheskogo Materializma. Moscow, Gospolitizdat, 1943.

Kommunist, Moscow.

Komsomol'skaya Pravda, Moscow.

Krasnaia Zvezda, Moscow.

Kravchenko, V. I Chose Freedom. New York, Charles Scribner's Sons, 1946.

Krokodil (Crocodile), Moscow.

Kuter, L. S. Airman at Yalta. New York, Duell, Sloan & Pearce, Inc., 1955.

Leahy, W. D. I Was There. New York, Whittlesey House, McGraw-Hill Book Company, Inc., 1950.

Leites, N. A Study of Bolshevism. Glencoe, Ill., The Free Press, 1953.

Lenin, V. I. Sochineniia (Papers). 4th ed. Moscow, Gospolitizdat, 1950.

Leningradskaya Pravda, Leningrad.

Literaturnaya Gazeta (Literary Gazette), Moscow.

McNeill, W. H. Survey of International Affairs, 1939–1946: America, Britain and Russia—Their Co-operation and

Conflict, 1941–1946. Royal Institute of International Affairs. London, Amen House, Oxford University Press, 1953.
Malaya Sovetskaia Entsiklopediia (Small Soviet Encyclopedia). Moscow, 1937.
Mikolajczyk, S. The Rape of Poland. New York, Whittlesey House, McGraw-Hill Book Company, Inc., 1948.
Minerals Yearbook, 1943. Washington, D.C., U.S. Government Printing Office, 1945.
Ministry of Culture of the USSR, Handbook for Entering Higher Educational Establishments. Moscow, February 5, 1957.
Moore, B. Terror and Progress in the USSR. Cambridge, Mass., Harvard University Press, 1954.
Moscow News (published in English), Moscow.
Nature, London.
Nesterenko, G. N., A. I. Sobolev, and Y. N. Shushkov. The Application of Atomic Engines in Aviation. Moscow, 1957.
New Times (published in English), Moscow.
The New York Times, New York.
Novy Mir, Moscow.
Obshchee Sobranie Akademii Nauk SSSR (General Assembly of Academy of Sciences of the USSR). September 25–30, 1943. Moscow, 1944.
Obshchee Sobranie Akademii Nauk SSSR, 14–17 oktiabria 1944 goda (General Session of the Academy of Sciences of the USSR, October 14–17, 1944). Moscow, Izd-vo Akademii Nauk SSSR., 1945.
Official Records, United Nations Atomic Energy Commission, New York.
Ogonek, Moscow.
Physics Today, New York.
Physik. Z. der Sovietunion, Moscow.
Pravda, Moscow.
Priroda (Nature), Moscow.
Proceedings of the First United Nations International Conference on the Peaceful Uses of Atomic Energy. Geneva, 1955.
Proceedings of the Second United Nations International Con-

ference on the Peaceful Uses of Atomic Energy. Geneva, 1958.

Proceedings of the Plenary Sessions, Session of the Academy of Sciences of the USSR on Peaceful Utilization of Atomic Energy, July 1–5, 1955. Moscow, 1955.

Promyshlenno-Ekonomicheskaya Gazeta, Moscow.

The Report of the Royal Commission . . . To Investigate . . . the Circumstances Surrounding the Communication . . . of Secret . . . Information to . . . a Foreign Power. Ottawa, His Majesty's Stationery Office, 1946.

Rosenman, S. I. Working with Roosevelt. New York, Harper & Brothers, 1952.

Sbornik zakonov SSSR i ukazov presidiuma Verkhovnogo Soveta SSSR, 1938–iiun 1944 gg (Handbook of Statutes of the USSR and Decrees of the Presidium of the Supreme Soviet, USSR, 1938–June 1944).

Science (printed by the USSR Society for Cultural Relations with Foreign Countries, VOKS), Moscow.

Shabad, T. Geography of the USSR. New York, Columbia University Press, 1951.

Sherwood, R. E. Roosevelt and Hopkins. New York, Harper & Brothers, 1948.

Smyth, H. D. A General Account of the Development of Methods Using Atomic Energy for Military Purposes. Washington, D.C., U.S. Government Printing Office, 1945.

Some Problems of the Theory of Cyclical Accelerators, Moscow, July 1955.

Soviet Economic Policy in Postwar Germany: A Collection of Papers by Former Soviet Officials. Research Program on the USSR. New York, 1953.

Soviet News (publication of the USSR Embassy at London).

Sovetskaia Aviatsiia, Moscow.

Sovetskii Flot, Moscow.

Sovetskaia Rossiia, Moscow.

Stalin, J. "Dialectical and Historical Materialism," in Voprosy Leninizma (Problems of Leninism), 11th ed. Moscow, Gospolitizdat, 1952.

Stettinius, E. R., Jr. Roosevelt and the Russians. Garden City, N.Y., Doubleday & Co., Inc., 1949.

Street, Lucie (ed.). I Married a Russian. New York, Emer-

son Books, 1947. This is a personal account of the lives
of Russian physicists in the 1930's.

Stroitel'naia Gazeta, Moscow.

Tekhnika Molodezhi (Techniques for Youth), Moscow, 1941.

Termoenergetika, Moscow.

Tokaev, G. A. Soviet Imperialism. London, Duckworth &
Co., 1954.

Transcript of the Gray Board Hearings, April 12, 1954 to
May 6, 1954. Washington, D.C., U.S. Government Printing Office, 1954.

Trud, Moscow.

Truman, H. S. Years of Decision. Garden City, N.Y., Doubleday & Company, Inc., 1955.

———. Years of Trial and Hope. Garden City, N.Y., Doubleday & Company, Inc., 1956.

Twentieth Session of the Communist Party of the Soviet
Union, Moscow, 1956.

U.S. Congress, Seventy-ninth Congress, First Session. Hearings Before the Special Committee on Atomic Energy,
United States Senate . . . Pursuant to Senate Resolution
179 . . . Creating a Special Committee To Investigate
Problems Relating to Atomic Energy, Part I. Washington, D.C., U.S. Government Printing Office, 1945.

U.S. Congress, Joint Committee on Atomic Energy, 82d Congress, 1st Session, "Soviet Atomic Espionage." Washington, D.C., U.S. Government Printing Office, 1951.

U.S. Congress, Joint Committee on Atomic Energy, 85th
Congress, 2d Session, *Report of the Underseas Warfare
Advisory Panel*. Washington, D.C., U.S. Government
Printing Office, August 1958.

Uspekhi Khimii (Progress of Chemistry), Moscow.

Uspekhi Fizicheskikh Nauk (Progress in Physical Sciences),
Moscow.

Vechernyaya Moskva, Moscow.

*Vedomosti Verkhovnogo Soveta (Records of the Supreme
Soviet)*, Moscow.

*Vestnik Akademii Nauk SSSR (Herald of the Academy of
Sciences of the USSR)*, Moscow.

Voyennaya Mysl', Moscow.

Vucinich, A. The Soviet Academy of Sciences. Stanford, Stanford University Press, 1956.

Weissberg, A. The Accused. New York, Simon & Schuster, Inc., 1951.

Zhurnal eksperimental 'noi i teoreticheskoi fiziki (Journal of Experimental and Theoretical Physics), Moscow.

Zhurnal Prikladnoi Khimii SSSR (Journal of Applied Chemistry of the USSR), Moscow.

INDEX

225

also Hydrogen bomb; Military implications

Atomic Energy Commission, U.S., 110, 123; and "Project Plowshare," 135, 138; shipments of isotopes to Russia, 164–65

Atomic Nucleus, All-Union Conference on the, 18, 28; and Conference on Questions of the Physics of the, 23

Atomic reactor, *see* Reactors

Baikov, Aleksandr, 98, 101, 103–4
Balabanov, Y., 162
Ballistic missiles, 157
Banská-Bystrica (Czechoslovakia), 149
Baruch Plan, 91, 96, 115
Belgian Congo, source of uranium for U.S., 26, 171
Beloyarskoye, 148–49
Berkeley, California, 19ff., 28, 198–201; Meshcheryakov's visit to, 188
Beria, Lavrentii, 54n., arrest of scientists, 109–10; control of atomic energy program, 176–77, 183–84
Beryllium, 53, 174, 192
Bikini, 188
Bismuth, 170
Blagonravov, A. A., 152
Blokhintsev, Dmitrii Ivanovich, 144, 189, 190
Bogdanov, Aleksandr, 4, 5
Bogolyubov, N. N., 189
Bohr's Institute, 58
Bomb tests (USA): 67, 127, 138–41, 188, 193; AEC announcements, 123, 127; first H-bomb, 127; Hanford, 122; implications of first test, 67; long-range monitoring program, 131–32; thermonuclear development, 124; Truman's announcement at Potsdam, 71, 78; U.S. Operation Ranger, 124
—— (USSR): 125, 126, 138–41, 188, 193; "dirty," 129; first Soviet test, 121, 123; hydrogen bomb, 124–25; lack of Soviet announcements,

124; second Soviet test, 124; Soviet lag in testing, 121–23; Stalin's reaction to first U.S. test, 78; suspension of, 130; test sites, 128
——, detection of, 123, 125, 131–32, 135, 139–41
Borkenau, Franz, 45
Bratsk, 138
Brookhaven, 190, 201–2
Budker, G. I., 193, 203, 208
Bukharin, Nikolai I., 8, 12, 13, 14, 204
Bush, Vannevar, 13
Byrnes, James F., 74, 78, 91–92, 118

Cambridge (England), 5, 16, 17
Canadian Spy Ring, 51, 55, 64, 66, 67–68, 78
CERN (European Organization for Nuclear Research), 190–91, 202
Chain reaction, 22, 63, 68, 111–15, 118–20; Baikov quoted on, 101; Fermi and first chain reaction, 100; Smyth quoted on, 53; Soviet scientists' contributions to, 16, 17, 22–23, 25
Cherenkov, Pavel, 17
Cyclotrons: early use of, 19; first in Europe, 20, 199; invention of, 198; Soviet, 19–21, 24–25, 32–33, 37, 59, 181, 183, 186, 188–89, 195, 200; U.S., 19–21, 40, 101–2, 188, 198; use in manufacturing radioactive isotopes, 163
Czechoslovakia, 149, 170, 171, 191

DCX (U.S. thermonuclear device), 208
Dollezhal', N. A., 144
Dolmatovskii, Yevgenii Aronovich, 133, 135
Don River, 149
Dubna, 179, 182, 188–89, 191, 200–202
Dzhelepov, V. P., 189

Einstein, Albert, 44, 84, 98
Eisenhower, Dwight D., 79, 87–88

OTHER VOLUMES OF
PUBLISHED

RAND RESEARCH

COLUMBIA UNIVERSITY PRESS, NEW YORK:

Soviet National Income and Product, 1940–48
    Abram Bergson and Hans Heymann, Jr., 1954
Soviet National Income and Product in 1928
    Oleg Hoeffding, 1954
Labor Productivity in Soviet and American Industry
    Walter Galenson, 1955

THE FREE PRESS, GLENCOE, ILLINOIS:

Psychosis and Civilization
    Herbert Goldhamer and Andrew W. Marshall, 1949
Soviet Military Doctrine
    Raymond L. Garthoff, 1953
A Study of Bolshevism
    Nathan Leites, 1953
Ritual of Liquidation: The Case of the Moscow Trials
    Nathan Leites and Elsa Bernaut, 1954

Two Studies in Soviet Controls: Communism and the Russian Peasant, and Moscow in Crisis
  Herbert S. Dinerstein and Leon Gouré, 1955
A Million Random Digits with 100,000 Normal Deviates
  The RAND Corporation, 1955

HARVARD UNIVERSITY PRESS, CAMBRIDGE, MASSACHUSETTS:

Smolensk Under Soviet Rule
  Merle Fainsod, 1958

MC GRAW-HILL BOOK COMPANY, INC., NEW YORK:

The Operational Code of the Politburo
  Nathan Leites, 1951
Air War and Emotional Stress: Psychological Studies of Bombing and Civilian Defense
  Irving L. Janis, 1951
Soviet Attitudes Toward Authority: An Interdisciplinary Approach to Problems of Soviet Character
  Margaret Mead, 1951
Mobilizing Resources for War: The Economic Alternatives
  Tibor Scitovsky, Edward Shaw, and Lorie Tarshis, 1951
The Organizational Weapon: A Study of Bolshevik Strategy and Tactics
  Philip Selznick, 1952
Introduction to the Theory of Games
  J. C. C. McKinsey, 1952
Weight-Strength Analysis of Aircraft Structures
  F. R. Shanley, 1952
The Compleat Strategyst: Being a Primer on the Theory of Games of Strategy
  J. D. Williams, 1954
Linear Programming and Economic Analysis
  Robert Dorfman, Paul A. Samuelson, and Robert M. Solow, 1958

THE MICROCARD FOUNDATION, MADISON, WISCONSIN:

The First Six Million Prime Numbers
    C. L. Baker and F. J. Gruenberger, 1959

NORTH-HOLLAND PUBLISHING COMPANY, AMSTERDAM, HOLLAND:

A Time Series Analysis of Interindustry Demands
    Kenneth J. Arrow and Marvin Hoffenberg, 1959

FREDERICK A. PRAEGER, PUBLISHERS, NEW YORK:

War and the Soviet Union: Nuclear Weapons and the Revolution in Soviet Military and Political Thinking
    H. S. Dinerstein, 1959

PRINCETON UNIVERSITY PRESS, PRINCETON, NEW JERSEY:

Approximations for Digital Computers
    Cecil Hastings, Jr., 1955
International Communication and Political Opinion: A Guide to the Literature
    Bruce Lannes Smith and Chitra M. Smith, 1956
Dynamic Programming
    Richard Bellman, 1957
The Berlin Blockade: A Study in Cold War Politics
    W. Phillips Davison, 1958
The French Economy and the State
    Warren C. Baum, 1958
Strategy in the Missile Age
    Bernard Brodie, 1959

PUBLIC AFFAIRS PRESS, WASHINGTON, D.C.:

The Rise of Khrushchev
    Myron Rush, 1958
Behind the Sputniks: A Survey of Soviet Space Science
    F. J. Krieger, 1958

RANDOM HOUSE, INC., NEW YORK:

Space Handbook: Astronautics and Its Applications
    Robert W. Buchheim and the Staff of The RAND Corporation, 1959

ROW, PETERSON AND COMPANY, EVANSTON, ILLINOIS:

German Rearmament and Atomic War: The Views of German Military and Political Leaders
    Hans Speier, 1957
West German Leadership and Foreign Policy
    Hans Speier and W. Phillips Davison (eds.), 1957
The House Without Windows: France Selects a President
    Constantin Melnik and Nathan Leites, 1958
Propaganda Analysis: A Study of Inferences Made from Nazi Propaganda in World War II
    Alexander L. George, 1959

STANFORD UNIVERSITY PRESS, STANFORD, CALIFORNIA:

Strategic Surrender: The Politics of Victory and Defeat
    Paul Kecskemeti, 1958
On the Game of Politics in France
    Nathan Leites, 1959

JOHN WILEY & SONS, INCORPORATED, NEW YORK:

Efficiency in Government through Systems Analysis: with Emphasis on Water Resource Development
    Roland N. McKean, 1958

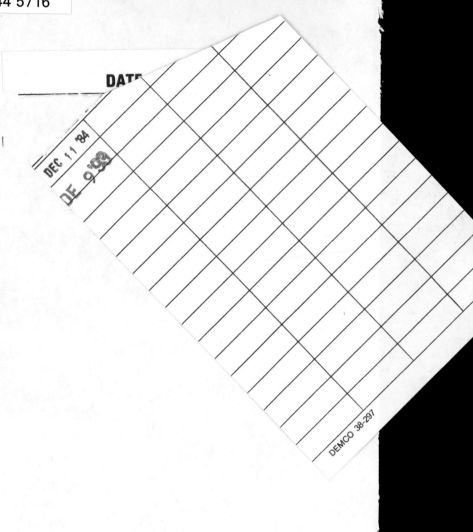